Originally published as:
The Giant Book of Trivia

by
Don Elmo
Illustrated by John Feeley
Edited by Marcia Diamond

Modern Publishing
A Division of Unisystems, Inc.
New York, New York 10022
Printed in Canada

Printed in Canada

Whatever time it is, it's time for trivia, America's favorite national pastime. In fact, no matter what national pastime you hear about or read about, you're boning up for trivia too!

Everyone plays it. Everyone enjoys stumping family and friends with teasers like "Was Bela Lugosi buried in his Dracula cape?", "How many managers had pennant-winning teams in both leagues?", or even "Who's the leader of the club that's made for you and me?"

So what time is it? It's time to turn the page—well, maybe you want to get a bowl of popcorn first—then enter the wonderful merry-go-round world of *TRIVIA!*

MEET THE FRIBBLE

Some people collect stamps or butterflies. I collect fribbles. The dictionary defines a fribble as a "trifling, frivolous thing." I say a fribble is any kind of super-trivia that only one person in a million knows. This means that once you learn it, you can stump at least 999,999 of your friends.

You'll find fribbles scattered throughout the book. Look for them. In the meantime, here are a few to get you in the right mood.

- The face of Captain Marvel as it first appeared in the comics was modeled after Fred MacMurray.

- Most American-model automobile horns beep in the same key—the key of F.

- Gary Cooper was a cowboy and cartoonist before going into show business.

START HERE

"The end begins," says one song. "The beguine begins," says another. No wonder people are confused! Wouldn't it be easier to say "Here we go"? I think so, so let's get going on our first trivia quiz about . . . what else . . . the beginning of things!

1. What is the first book of the Bible? What are the first three words?

2. Who began his major film work when George Raft refused the lead in HIGH SIERRA because it meant dying at the end?

3. Who wrote the song "Begin the Beguine"?

4. What famous "gothic" novel begins: "Last night I dreamt I went to Manderley again"?

5. What famous American document begins: "We the people"?

6. Gene Wilder and Donald Sutherland play two sets of twins in a swashbuckling comedy about the beginning of the French Revolution. What is the name of the movie?

7. Clark Gable is a lawyer who falls for Sophia Loren in what movie?

8. Which World War began with the assassination of Archduke Francis Ferdinand of Austria-Hungary?

9. What war began with the "shot heard round the world"?

10. Where was the shot in #9 fired?

START HERE

(Answers)

1. GENESIS . . . "In the beginning . . ."

2. Humphrey Bogart

3. Cole Porter

4. REBECCA

5. Preamble of the U.S. Constitution

6. START THE REVOLUTION WITHOUT ME

7. IT STARTED IN NAPLES

8. World War I

9. The American Revolution   10. Lexington and Concord

HEY, SPORT—
DON'T CALL ME NICK!

Here's a quiz about sports nicknames from the whole wide world of sports. The object of the game is to read the nickname then give the actual name of the player.

Sure, the rules are easy. But let's see how many you know before you go dubbing me DIZZY DON.

1. Galloping Ghost
2. Georgia Peach
3. Pélé
4. The Iron Horse
5. The Lip
6. The Four Horsemen
7. The Norwegian Doll
8. Joltin' Joe
9. Wild Bull of the Pampas
10. The Manassa Mauler

HEY, SPORT— DON'T CALL ME NICK!

(Answers)

1. Harold (Red) Grange
2. Ty Cobb
3. Edson Arantes do Nascimento
4. Lou Gehrig
5. Leo Durocher
6. Jim Crowley, Don Miller, Elmer Layden, Harry Stuhldreher
7. Sonja Henie
8. Joe DiMaggio
9. Luis Firpo
10. Jack Dempsey

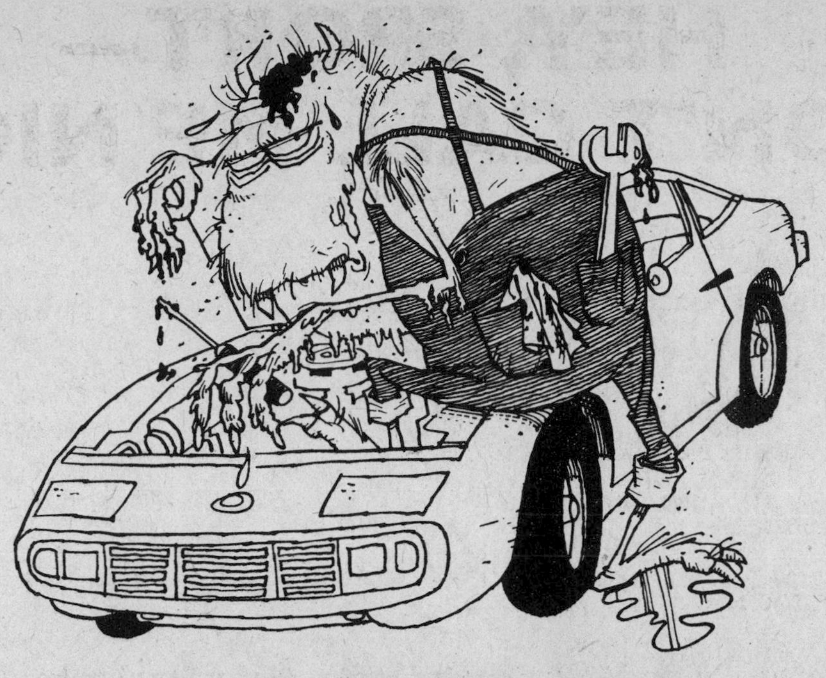

VA-ROOM!

Screech! Squeak! Here it comes . . . *zap* . . . around the hairpin turns . . . breaking all known records. It's . . . it's . . . you tell me. Here are some names, dates, and facts about car racing that should separate the jalopy-heads from the true blue fans.

1. Where and when was the first Indianapolis 500 held? Who won?
2. Against what do cars race at Bonneville Salt Flats, Utah?
3. Who was the first man to drive over 400 m.p.h.?
4. What do the Sebring, Mille Miglia, and Le Mans races have in common?
5. What does NASCAR stand for?
6. The most famous early race car driver, who drove the "Number 999" for Henry Ford, was ___________ ?
7. Who won the Grand Prix in 1969, 1971, and 1973?
8. Where were the first U.S. automobile races held?
9. What is the distinguishing feature of a stock car race?
10. Who won the Indy 500 in 1969 with his STP Hawk-Ford?

VA-ROOM!

(Answers)

1. Memorial Day, 1911 . . . Indianapolis, Indiana . . . Ray Harroun (500 miles in 6:42:08 or 74.59 m.p.h.)

2. Cars race against the clock rather than each other, timing acceleration and speed on a one-quarter mile straight track.

3. John R. Cobb

4. They're all sports car races.

5. National Association for Stock Car Auto Racing

6. Barney Oldfield

7. Jackie Stewart

8. In Narragansett, Rhode Island—top speeds were about 10 m.p.h. so as races they left something to be desired.

9. The cars are standard-model coupes or sedans rather than specially-built race cars.

10. Mario Andretti

ACCORDING TO AESOP

Aesop was most likely a Greek slave some 2500 years ago. If he were alive today, he'd probably be a talk show host, interviewing animals. There is a moral to this story: If you want to interview talking animals on TV, hang in there . . . .

1. What happened to the dog who was carrying a piece of meat in his mouth when he saw his reflection in a stream?
2. When the wolf was choking on a small bone and the crane removed it with his long beak and neck, what reward did the wolf give in return?
3. When the fox saw the crow with a piece of cheese in its beak, what did he say to make her drop the cheese?
4. How did the little mouse escape being eaten by the lion? How did the little mouse rescue the lion some time later?
5. What is the moral of the fable about the little mouse and the lion?
6. The hares were fed up with always fleeing danger, and decided to jump in the lake and end it all, when they learned what valuable lesson?
7. When the wolf passed alongside a house, a little goat on the roof jeered at it. What was the wolf's reaction?
8. What happened to the fox who saw a bunch of grapes on a vinc but discovered, after several attempts, that they were just beyond his reach?
9. What is the moral of the story about the wolf in sheep's clothing?
10. Who starved when winter came, the grasshopper or the ant?

ACCORDING TO AESOP

(Answers)

1. He thought he saw another dog with a second piece of meat, became greedy and snarled to scare the other dog away to have both dinners to himself. When he snarled, his own meat fell into the stream and sank.

2. The wolf said it was reward enough to put your head in a wolf's mouth and take it out again in safety.

3. He said she had a beautiful voice and asked her to sing.

4. The mouse promised the lion, "let me go and one day I will return the favor." When the lion was later caught in a trap, the mouse set him free by gnawing through the ropes.

5. Little friends can be great friends.

6. As they ran toward the lake, the frogs scampered away willy-nilly in terror, showing the hares that there's always someone worse off than you are.

7. The wolf said it is easy to be brave from a safe distance.

8. The sulking fox consoled himself by saying "they were probably sour grapes anyway."

9. Appearances can be deceiving.

10. The ant stored up food all summer long while the grasshopper lolled around. When winter came, the grasshopper had nothing to eat.

CRIME-SOLVERS CONVENTION

None of these world-famous sleuths can take a bow without your help. So name the crime-solver who came through in each of these cases, and if you get all ten, you're entitled to take a bow yourself . . . .

1. Who flushed out the felon in FIVE RED HERRINGS?
2. Who was the sleuth in THE HOUSE WITHOUT A KEY?
3. In THE MALTESE FALCON?
4. In TOO MANY CROOKS?
5. In FUNERALS ARE FATAL?
6. In the movie version of FUNERALS ARE FATAL?
7. In THE LEDGER and THE BAIT?
8. In the Christie short story DEATH ON THE NILE?
9. In the Christie novel DEATH ON THE NILE?
10. In FAREWELL, MY LOVELY?

CRIME-SOLVERS CONVENTION

(Answers)

1. Lord Peter Wimsey 2. Charlie Chan 3. Sam Spade 4. Nero Wolfe

5. Hercule Poirot . . . the book is also called AFTER THE FUNERAL

6. Jane Marple . . . the movie is MURDER AT THE GALLOP

7. Christie Opara 8. Parker Pyne

9. Hercule Poirot

10. Philip Marlowe

HE-NANIGANS

*She*nanigans and *mis*chief are like *hur*ricanes—they can't help giving the impression that somehow, somewhere, there's a woman behind them all, kicking up a fuss.

So here's a quiz to set the record straight—10 teasers about trouble that's strictly *man*-made . . . .

1. Name the "Robin Goodfellow" imp in Shakespeare's MIDSUMMER NIGHT'S DREAM.

2. Which fairy tale cat uses his wits and wiles to get his master a castle, a fortune, and a princess?

3. Who played TV's DENNIS THE MENACE?

4. In THE MUSIC MAN, who warns that *trouble* is coming to River City in the form of a pool table?

5. What TV show gave us Eddie Haskel, one of the champion wiseguys of the universe? Who played the role?

6. What are the names of the Katzenjammer Kids?

7. In which Marx Brothers movie do Groucho, Harpo, Chico and Zeppo have to pretend to be Maurice Chevalier to get off the luxury liner on which they've stowed away?

8. Who played LITTLE RASCALS Alfalfa, Spanky, and Jackie?

9. What's the nickname of Jack Dawkins in OLIVER TWIST?

10. What is Leo Gorcey's role in THE EAST SIDE KIDS series? In the BOWERY BOYS series?

HE-NANIGANS

(Answers)

1. Puck
2. Puss in Boots
3. Jay North
4. Professor Harold Hill
5. LEAVE IT TO BEAVER . . . Ken Osmond
6. Hans and Fritz
7. MONKEY BUSINESS
8. Carl Switzer . . . George Emmett McFarland . . . Jackie Cooper
9. The Artful Dodger
10. Ethelbert ''Muggs'' McGinnis . . . Terrence Aloysius ''Slip'' Mahoney

AROUND THE WORLD IN 80 FLICKS—FIRST LEG

Here we go on a round-the-world adventure based on the movies America loves best. Just match the flick with its geographic setting, then climb aboard for the next leg of your junket. Remember, there'll be 80 films by the end of the book—ten to a quiz. Look for them!

1. WUTHERING HEIGHTS	a. Vienna
2. SATURDAY NIGHT FEVER	b. Yorkshire moors
3. SERIAL	c. Berlin
4. BON VOYAGE, CHARLIE BROWN	d. Vietnam
5. CABARET	e. Brooklyn
6. GREEN DOLPHIN STREET	f. Texas
7. GIANT	g. Northern California
8. FROM HERE TO ETERNITY	h. New Zealand
9. APOCALYPSE NOW	i. Honolulu
10. THE THIRD MAN	j. France

Answers:

1b, 2e, 3g, 4j, 5c, 6h, 7f, 8i, 9d, 10a.

EVERLAST

"I AM THE GREATEST!"

Want to be the "Greatest?" Make these questions float like a butterfly and sting the answers like a bee.

1. What was Muhammad Ali's previous name?

2. Did Ali ever fight in the Olympics? If so, how did he do?

3. Which world heavyweight champion did he defeat in 1964 to win the crown?

4. In 1967, the title was taken away from Ali for what reason?

5. In 1970, after a 3½-year layoff, Ali was allowed to fight again. Who was his first opponent and how did he do?

6. In 1971, Ali fought for the title again. Who was his opponent and how did he do this time?

7. When was the next time Ali fought for the title? Who did he fight? Who won?

8. Who was the only fighter ever to break Ali's jaw?

9. Who was the only man to take the title from Muhammad Ali?

10. In 1978, Ali again fought for the title. Who did he fight and what was the outcome?

"I AM THE GREATEST!"

(Answers)

1. Cassius Clay, Jr.

2. Yes. Ali fought in the 1960 Olympics and won the light heavyweight gold medal

3. Sonny Liston

4. He refused to be inducted into the U.S. Army.

5. Jerry Quarry was tko-ed in the third round.

6. Joe Frazier defeated Muhammad by unanimous decision.

7. 1974 . . . George Foreman . . . Ali regained the title by knocking him out in the eighth round.

8. Ken Norton

9. Leon Spinks in 1978

10. He defeated Leon Spinks by a unanimous decision to win the crown for an unprecedented third time.

LOVE IS

Among other things, love is a four-letter word. But songwriters will try to tell you different . . .

1. Nominated for an Academy Award, "Love Is" is the opening song of what movie?

2. So what if the Rockies crumble and Gibralter tumbles! A haunting tune from George and Ira Gershwin assures us that our "love is . . .

3. A Cole Porter song asks the musical question "What Is This Thing Called Love?" What is the answer?

4. In now-forgotten songs, Richard Rogers has informed us that "Love's Intense in Tents" and "Love Is My Friend." But in one of his most popular ballads, "Falling In Love With Love" is two absolutely miserable things. What are they?

5. In the title song of the movie that gave us "Donkey Serenade," love dies while it is gleaming because it is like . . .

6. The Academy-Award-winning song of 1955 came from a poignant non-musical movie about East meeting West. The movie starred Jennifer Jones and William Holden. What is the song? The movie? Love?

7. In one of Bing Crosby's first great hits, he remarks that his sweetie is better than Venus de Milo because his sweetie can hug him back. While all this hugging is going on, "Love Is . . .

8. According to the longest-running Broadway musical of the 1930s—all about a Presidential election campaign—what is love doing?

9. What's wonderful, marvelous, awfully nice, and paradise?

10. In the song "I Love Paris," what oh what is given as the reason for why oh why?

LOVE IS

(Answers)

1. Love is THE TENDER TRAP.
2. Here to Stay
3. There is no answer. The entire song is devoted to asking the question.
4. Falling for make believe and playing the fool
5. A FIREFLY
6. All three answers are the same: "Love Is A Many-Splendored Thing."
7. Just Around The Corner
8. "Love Is Sweeping The Country"
9. That you should care for me . . . in the song "'S Wonderful"
10. Because my love is near

FULL COURT

It's roundball time! Put all ten through the hoop and you will be an all-star.

1. Who scored the most points in a single game? How many?
2. Who scored the most consecutive points in a game and how many?
3. Who scored the most points in a single season?
4. Who has the single-season record for assists?
5. Who has the single-season record for steals?
6. What were the most points scored in a single game by one team? Which team was it?
7. What team has won the most games in a single season?
8. What team lost the most games in a single season?
9. What team has the longest winning streak?
10. Which team has won the most division titles, and how many?

FULL COURT

(Answers)

1. Wilt Chamberlain . . . 100 points . . . Philadelphia vs. the New York Knicks on March 2, 1962

2. Wilt Chamberlain . . . 15 consecutive points . . . Philadelphia vs. Baltimore on March 20, 1966

3. Wilt Chamberlain . . . 4029 points in the 1961-62 season while playing for Philadelphia

4. Kevin Porter . . . 1099 . . . while playing for the Detroit Pistons in the 1978-79 season

5. Don Buse . . . 281 . . . playing with the Indiana Pacers in the 1976-77 season

6. 173 points by Boston (vs. Minneapolis) on February 27, 1959

7. Los Angeles Lakers in the 1971-72 season . . . 69 games

8. Philadelphia 76ers in the 1972-73 season . . . lost 73 games

9. Los Angeles Lakers . . . winning 33 games from November 5, 1971 through January 7, 1972

10. The Boston Celtics . . . 15

COME ON BREAKER

Mercy sakes. Here's a quiz that's right up your CB show-off lane. If you know all ten you're a gear-jamming buddy for sure, and the bubblegum boys can eat your dust.

May the great bird of paradise drop eighty eights all over your rig. Now back to you cause we gone. (88s are love and kisses.)

1. In CB talk, what are *green stamps* or *trading stamps*?
2. What's a *beaver*?
3. What's a *handle*?
4. What's a *pregnant roller skate*?
5. What's a *pair of nickels*?
6. What does *wilco* mean?
7. What is a *bear in the air* or a *bear in the sky*?
8. What's *Colorado kool aid*?
9. What's a *meat wagon* or a *bone box*?
10. What are *greenies*, *coupons*, or *paperwork*?

COME ON BREAKER

(Answers)

1. Money
2. A female
3. A CBers' code or identification name
4. A Volkswagen
5. The 55 mile-per-hour speed limit
6. *Will* comply . . . meaning that *roger wilco* translates *yes, will comply*
7. A police helicopter
8. Beer, particularly Coor's beer
9. An ambulance
10. Speeding tickets

KONG'S KORNER

Can you answer these questions about the world's most famous visitor to the top of the Empire State Building? If he had taken the elevator and paid admission, do you think the authorities would have let him enjoy the view in peace?

1. In the original KING KONG, why did Carl Denham, Jack Driscoll, and Ann Darrow sail to Kong's island?
2. What was the name of the tramp steamer that took them there?
3. Who played the roles of Denham, Driscoll, and Darrow?
4. What was the island called? Where was it located?
5. What was the name of the first sequel to KING KONG?
6. In the 1976 remake, why does the ship sail to Kong's island?
7. What building does King Kong fall from in the remake?
8. Who played the actress in the remake?
9. In the last scene, why does she plead with King Kong *not* to put her down?
10. What are the final words spoken in the original KING KONG?

KONG'S KORNER

(Answers)

1. To make a movie
2. The Venture
3. Robert Armstrong, Bruce Cabot, Fay Wray
4. Skull Island . ... in the Indian Ocean far west of Sumatra
5. SON OF KONG
6. To find oil
7. The twin towers of the World Trade Center
8. Jessica Lange
9. She knows that the planes won't attack Kong as long as he's holding her . . . but that he will be killed as soon as he releases her.
10. "It wasn't the airplanes. It was beauty killed the beast."

BAKER STREET DOZEN

At last! Your chance to test your knowledge of the stately Holmes of England. How? Elementary—be *de*deucedly clever . . .

1. What was Sherlock's home address?
2. Who was his roommate?
3. Who was the creator of Sherlock Holmes?
4. Where and when did Sherlock meet his "death," and why didn't he actually die?
5. In which Sherlock Holmes adventure did Sherlock and Watson first meet?
6. What instrument did Holmes play?
7. Which hideous creature inhabited the ship Matilda?
8. What do Oliver Wendell Holmes and Joseph Bell have in common?
9. In the movies, who played Sherlock Holmes to Nigel Bruce's Doctor Watson?
10. What was the name of Sherlock's older brother?
11. In which Holmes adventure will you find Irene Adler?
12. Where did LeStrade work?

BAKER STREET DOZEN

(Answers)

1. 221B Baker Street, N.W.1, London, England

2. John H. Watson, M.D.

3. Sir Arthur Conan Doyle

4. Holmes and his arch-enemy Professor Moriarty fought "to the death" on Reichenbach Falls on May 4, 1891. Doyle, who was tired of writing Holmes adventures, at first thought this would be the end of the world's most famous consulting detective. But public pressure was so great that he had to write a sequel in which Holmes escaped death.

5. A STUDY IN SCARLET

6. The violin

7. The giant rat of Sumatra

8. Each is believed by different scholars to be the original inspiration for Sherlock Holmes.

9. Basil Rathbone

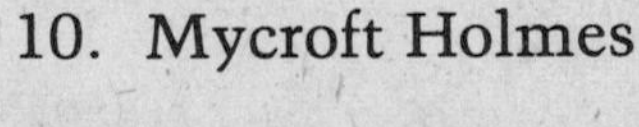

10. Mycroft Holmes

11. A SCANDAL IN BOHEMIA

12. Inspector LeStrade worked for Scotland Yard.

TORCH TEASERS

Do you want to win a gold medal? Just answer these teasers about those great events that set the world on fire every four years.

1. When and where were the first modern-day summer Olympics held?

2. The U.S. Olympic basketball team has won every gold medal except two. Which year did they lose and who won?

3. Which athlete has won the most gold medals in one Olympic competition? What year? What sport?

4. Who's the only heavyweight boxer ever to win the gold medal twice?

5. Who has the Olympic record in the men's 100 meter dash and what was his time?

6. Since 1908, the U.S. has had only one gold medal in the marathon race. Who won it and in what year?

7. In 1912, Britain won the gold medal in the men's 400 meter relay (in track). Since then, only one other team has beaten the U.S.A. Which team was it and when was it?

8. Who holds the Olympic record for the long jump and how far did he jump?

9. Who won the men's triple jump in three separate Olympics and what country did he represent?

TORCH TEASERS

(Answers)

1. 1896 in Athens, Greece
2. The U.S.S.R. won in 1972 and Yugoslavia won in 1980. The U.S. did not participate in 1980.
3. Mark Spitz won seven gold medals in 1972, swimming.
4. Telafilo Stevenson (Cuba) won it in 1972 and again in 1976
5. James Hines (U.S.A.) . . . 9.9 seconds (1968)
6. Frank Shorter in 1972
7. West Germany in 1960
8. Bob Beamon (U.S.A.) . . . 29 feet 2½ inches (1968)
9. V. Saneev of the U.S.S.R.

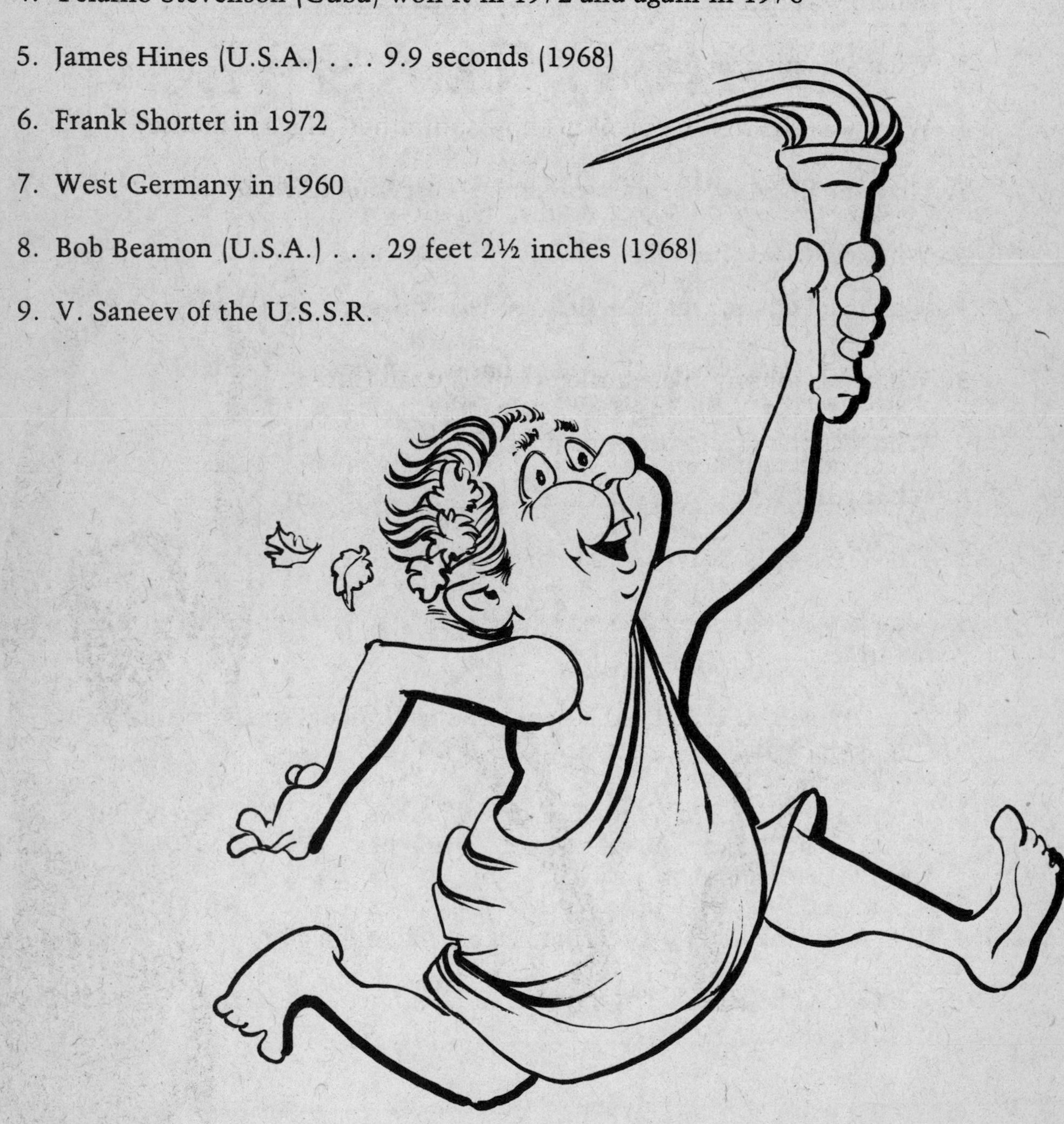

TARZAN SWINGS

Tarzan, Tarzan, he's our man. If he can't stump you, no one can. Or can he? If you really know your Tarzan well enough to swing through the trees with him, maybe you can avoid these stumps.

1. Who were his titled English parents?
2. Where was he born?
3. What was his real name?
4. What was the first name of his human mother? His ape mother?
5. Give the full name of the woman who became his mate.
6. What color was her hair?
7. Who was the first movie Tarzan?
8. What was Johnny Weismuller's first Tarzan film?
9. Who was the creator of Tarzan?
10. What city was founded by the person named in #9?

TARZAN SWINGS

(Answers)

1. Lord and Lady Greystoke
2. In Africa
3. John Clayton
4. Alice . . . Kala
5. Jane Porter
6. She was blonde in the books but in most of the films she was brunette.
7. Elmo Lincoln
8. TARZAN OF THE APES (1932)
9. Edgar Rice Burroughs
10. Tarzana, California

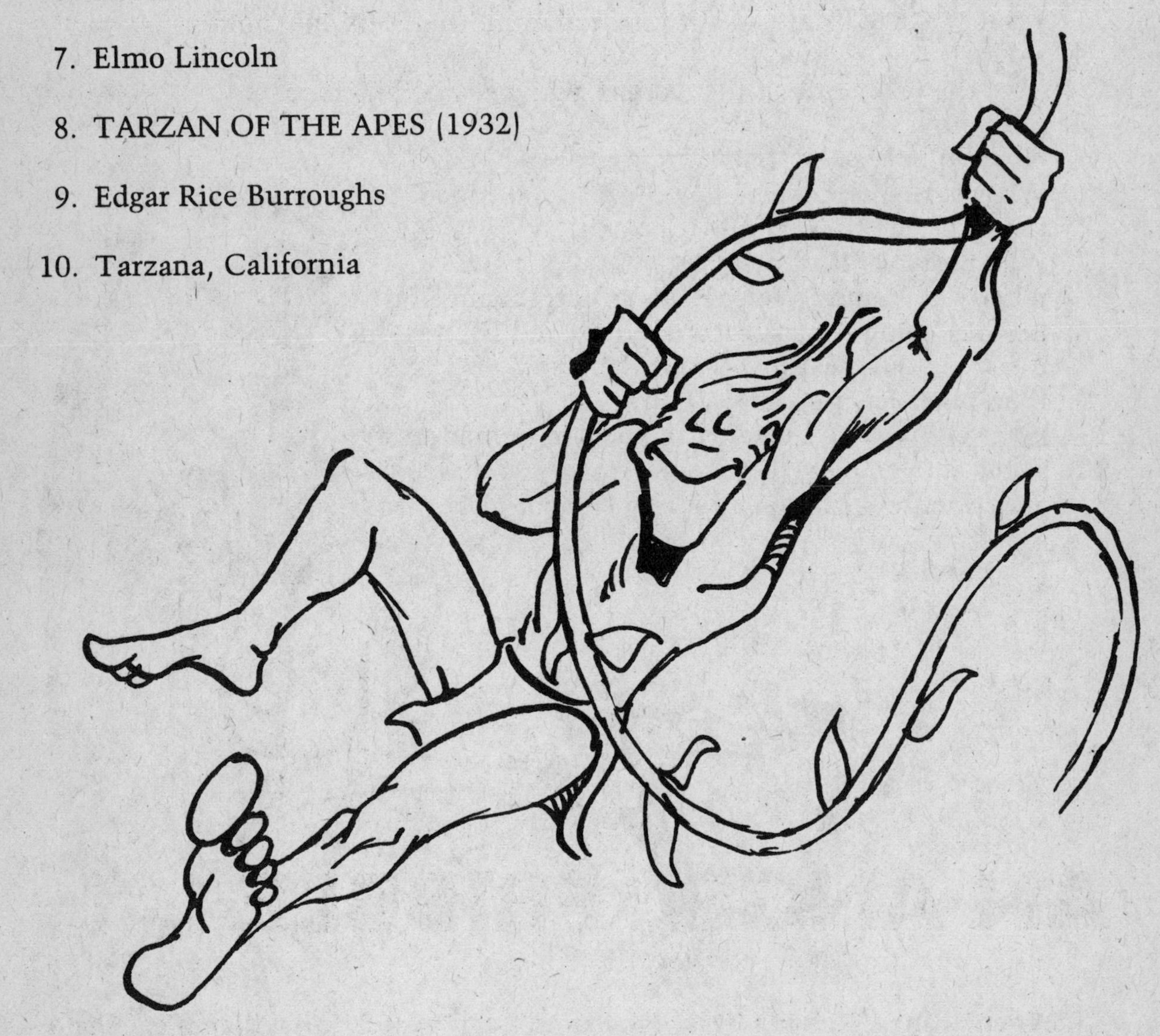

DATE WITH THE ANGELS

Charlie's the smart one—he stays out of sight. Because anyone hanging around these bombshells is headed for a few million megatons of danger, which is why this quiz receives a K ("KA-BOOM") rating from the Don Elmo Official Review Board.

1. Name the actress who plays or played—Sabrina.
2. —Jill?
3. —Kelly?
4. —Kris?
5. —Tiffany?
6. What is the name of the Angels' unseen boss?
7. Who provides the voice of Charlie?
8. Besides being Angels, how are Kris and Jill related?
9. Who plays John Bosley, Charlie's assistant?
10. What actress played Antonia Blake, boss of a detective agency affectionately known as Toni's Boys, in one episode?

AN ANGEL FRIBBLE

When Tanya Roberts was chosen to play Angel Julie Richards, she'd already appeared in VEGA$ and been seriously considered for Bo Derek's role in *10.* With those credentials and her exceptional good looks, no wonder she beat out some thousand other girls for the role— for *$22,500* per episode.

DATE WITH THE ANGELS

(Answers)

1. Kate Jackson
2. Farrah Fawcett-Majors
3. Jaclyn Smith
4. Cheryl Ladd
5. Shelley Hack
6. Charlie Townsend
7. John Forsythe
8. Kris Munroe is Jill Munroe's younger sister.
9. David Doyle
10. Barbara Stanwyck

FAMILY FUN

Don Elmo's Theory of Relativity states that you have to be a genius to remember who's related to whom. For instance, what's the relationship between . . . .

1. Larry Hagman and Mary Martin?
2. Sally Field and Jock Mahoney?
3. Warren Beatty and Shirley MacLaine?
4. Joan Fontaine and Olivia de Havilland
5. Jack Jones and Allan Jones?
6. Dina Merrill and Barbara Hutton?
7. Theodore Roosevelt and Franklin Roosevelt?
8. Maureen O'Sullivan and Mia Farrow?
9. Abigail Van Buren and Ann Landers?
10. Peter Graves and James Arness?

FAMILY FUN

(Answers)

1. She's his mother.
2. He's her father.
3. They're brother and sister.
4. They're sisters.
5. Allan is Jack's father.
6. They're cousins.
7. They're fifth cousins.
8. Maureen is Mia's mother.
9. They're twin sisters.
10. They're brothers.

KNIGHTLY DAYS

Legend has it that 150 knights sat around King Arthur's Round Table—but relax, you only have to name a few of them for this quiz. As for the rest of the questions, you'll do okay if you've seen even a few of the movies about the days when knighthood was in flower.

1. What was the name of King Arthur's sword?

2. Who was his wife and queen?

3. Who was his wicked nephew?

4. What was the name of his sorcerer?

5. What was his kingdom called?

6. Who was the knight who betrayed him by falling in love with Mrs. King Arthur?

7. What was the sacred quest that only the purest knights of the Round Table could undertake?

8. According to legend, who was the only knight pure enough to complete the quest?

9. In the Broadway musical CAMELOT, who played the king, the queen, and the knight who loved the queen?

10. In the movie version of the musical, who played those same roles?

KNIGHTLY DAYS

(Answers)

1. Excalibur

2. Guinevere . . . also spelled Guenevere

3. Modred . . . also spelled Mordred

4. Merlin . . . also spelled Merlyn

5. Camelot

6. Sir Lancelot of the Lake

7. Finding the Holy Grail

8. Of all the knights who came close, including Sir Percivale, Sir Gawain, Sir Bors, and Sir Lancelot, only Sir Galahad saw the Holy Grail.

9. Richard Burton was King Arthur,
   Julie Andrews was Queen Guenevere,
   Robert Goulet was Sir Lancelot.

10. Richard Harris was the king,
    Vanessa Redgrave was Guinevere,
    Franco Nero was Lancelot.

ALIAS MR. WONDERFUL

Wonderful, schmunderful, none of these TV characters can get a credit card under his famous alias.

If you can supply all 10 TV names (not the names of the actors who played them) you'll . . . you'll . . . *um, ehr* . . . you'll help increase the national debt.

So don't take this quiz if you already gave at the office, or anywhere else.

1. THE MILLIONAIRE
2. THE LONE RANGER
3. THE RIFLEMAN
4. THE SAINT
5. THE SIX MILLION DOLLAR MAN
6. ZORRO
7. DAKTARI
8. THE FUGITIVE
9. BACHELOR FATHER
10. THE PRISONER

ALIAS MR. WONDERFUL

(Answers)

1. John Beresford Tipton

2. John Reid
3. Lucas McCain
4. Simon Templar
5. Colonel Steve Austin
6. Don Diego de la Vega
7. Dr. Marsh Tracy . . . "Daktari" is Swahili for *doctor*.
8. Dr. Richard Kimble
9. Bentley Gregg
10. Number 6 . . . though it is possible to speculate that THE PRISONER is an unofficial continuation of SECRET AGENT, in which case both *The Prisoner* and *Number 6* are John Drake.

SEEING DOUBLE

Double roles—that's Hollywood's way of giving the public twice as much of a good thing. And there's an added bonus in it for you. If you suspect you don't like the performer playing the double role, it's your way of finding out twice as fast.

Now, on the double, supply the names of the stars who played two or more roles in each of the following feature films.

1. THE DARK MIRROR
2. KISSIN' COUSINS
3. A STOLEN LIFE
4. THE MOUSE THAT ROARED
5. THE PARENT TRAP
6. KIND HEARTS AND CORONETS
7. WONDER MAN
8. THE PRISONER OF ZENDA (1922)
9. THE PRISONER OF ZENDA (1937)
10. THE PRISONER OF ZENDA (1952)

SEEING DOUBLE

(Answers)

1. Olivia de Havilland
2. Elvis Presley
3. Bette Davis
4. Peter Sellers (3 roles)
5. Hayley Mills
6. Alec Guinness (8 roles)
7. Danny Kaye
8. Ramon Novarro
9. Ronald Colman
10. Stewart Granger

IN A SPIN

A spin-off is when characters from one popular TV show turn up in a show of their own. Sometimes the original actors continue in their roles, sometimes not—and sometimes, more than a decade later—because nothing is too far-fetched in TV-land U.S.A.

1. On what TV show did Mork from Ork first appear?
2. What show introduced the Jeffersons before they moved on up to the East Side with a series of their own?
3. The same show that introduced Mork gave us __________ and __________, the boy-crazy roommates who work in Shotz Brewery.
4. She left Mel's diner to start an eatery—and a show—of her own. What show did she leave? What show did she leave it to star in?
5. Before he became Gomer Pyle, U.S.M.C., Gomer worked in a gas station in what town on which show?
6. From an adorable but definitely minor part in BEWITCHED, Samantha and Darrin's daughter grew up to star in ____________ .
7. One of the doctors from M*A*S*H continues his practice state-side on ____________ .
8. This sitcom spun-off the sitcoms PHYLLIS and RHODA, which didn't last, and the dramatic series LOU GRANT, which did.
9. Perhaps TV's first spin-off, PETE AND GLADYS spun out of which long-running series of the 1950s?
10. Before they moved to KNOTS LANDING, they were J.R.'s kinfolk on DALLAS. They who?

IN A SPIN

(Answers)

1. HAPPY DAYS
2. ALL IN THE FAMILY
3. LAVERNE & SHIRLEY
4. ALICE . . . FLO
5. Mayberry, North Carolina . . . THE ANDY GRIFFITH SHOW
6. TABITHA (played by Erin and Diane Murphy in BEWITCHED and Lisa Hartman in TABITHA).
7. TRAPPER JOHN, M.D. (played by Wayne Rogers in M*A*S*H and Pernell Roberts in TRAPPER JOHN, M.D.).
8. THE MARY TYLER MOORE SHOW
9. DECEMBER BRIDE
10. Gary and Val Ewing (Ted Shackelford and Joan Van Ark)

ORIENT EXPRESS

The world's most famous, exotic, and romantic train has just recently gone the way of the dinosaur and the dodo. But even out of business, it will never become the world's most extinct railroad. Not when its magic lives on in so many imaginations. Or does it . . . ?

1. Which of these cities was not along one of the routes of the Orient Express? Athens, Venice, Berlin, Brussels, Nuremberg, Budapest, Bucharest, Warsaw, Istanbul?

2. Why didn't the Orient Express go to Constantinople after 1930?

3. When did it make its final run?

4. What English movie concerns Valya and Zurta on the Orient Express? What are they looking for?

5. Disguised as a butterfly collector, Lord Baden-Powell frequently traveled the Orient Express in his little-publicized role of spy. For what is he better known?

6. Agatha Christie's novel set aboard this train is called what in America? What in Britain?

7. Ditto Graham Greene's novel. What is the U.S. title? What is the British title?

8. In which James Bond adventure does the climax occur aboard the Orient Express?

9. Which Eric Ambler thriller involves a master criminal whose activities are closely tied to the Orient Express?

10. Though not Hitchcock's only train-bound movie, this classic stars Michael Redgrave and Dame May Whitty.

ORIENT EXPRESS

(Answers)

1. Berlin

2. Constantinople was renamed Istanbul in March 1930.

3. Though trains had been running shorter routes and with fewer services for over a decade, the *final* appearance came in May of 1977, ending the 94-year history of the fabulous Orient Express.

4. SLEEPING CAR TO TRIESTE . . . Valya and Zurta are after a secret political diary.

5. He was the founder of the Boy Scouts.

6. MURDER ON THE CALAIS COACH . . . MURDER ON THE ORIENT EXPRESS

7. ORIENT EXPRESS . . . STAMBOUL TRAIN

8. FROM RUSSIA, WITH LOVE

9. THE MASK OF DIMITRIOS

10. THE LADY VANISHES

SEZ WHO?

You don't have to be an astrologer to turn to these heavenly bodies for advice. But the question is, do you really identify the product with the star who endorses it? Or do you just remember seeing stars? Take this matching quiz and find out.

1. Rita Moreno	*a.* L'eggs
2. Juliet Prowse	*b.* Short & Sassy
3. Susan Ford	*c.* Cordoba
4. Ricardo Montalban	*d.* Pepsodent
5. Robert Young	*e.* Subaru
6. Bill Cosby	*f.* Alka Seltzer
7. Dorothy Hamill	*g.* Sanka
8. Joyce DeWitt	*h.* Jell-O
9. Sammy Davis Jr.	*i.* Alpo
10. Lorne Greene	*j.* Undie-L'eggs

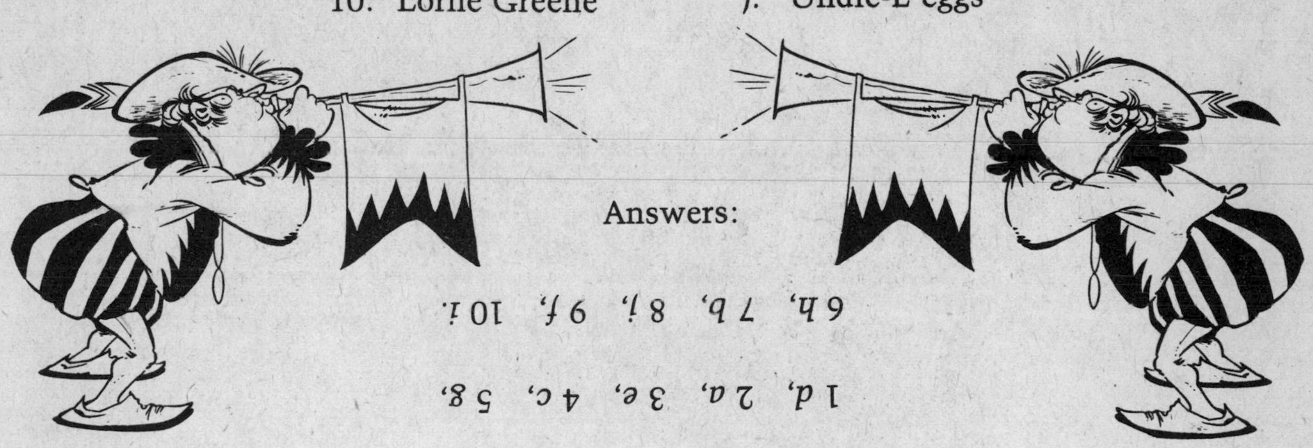

Answers:

1*d*, 2*a*, 3*e*, 4*c*, 5*g*,

6*h*, 7*b*, 8*j*, 9*f*, 10*i*.

JEFFERSO
HIGH SCHOO

HAPPY DAYS

Now, what could this quiz possibly be about? First hint: it's about the TV show pictured to the left. Second hint: If you need a second hint, this isn't your quiz. But anyhow, have a happy day.

1. What are Potsie's and Ralph's last names, and who plays each character?

2. Where does the gang hang out?

3. Who owns number two above?

4. Who plays Pinky Tuscadero? Who plays her sister, and what is that character's name?

5. To what lodge does Howard Cunningham belong?

6. What's Richie's major at college? What's Potsie's?

7. Name the three children of Howard and Marion Cunningham.

8. Where did Fonzie go to high school? Did he ever graduate?

9. When Richie wanted to publish a story about Fonzie's secret fear, it nearly wrecked their friendship. What was the Fonz afraid of?

10. The play GREASE and the movie AMERICAN GRAFFITI both set the stage for the TV series HAPPY DAYS. Everyone knows that—but not many people can tell you what LOVE, AMERICAN STYLE and a sketch called ''Love and the Happy Day'' had to do with it. Do you know?

HAPPY DAYS

(Answers)

1. Anson Williams plays Warren (Potsie) Weber . . Donny Most plays Ralph Malph

2. Arnold's Drive-In

3. Arnold was, but now it belongs to Alfred Delvecchio.

4. Roz Kelly . . . Suzi Quatro plays her sister Leather.

5. The Leopard Lodge

6. Richie majors in journalism, Potsie in psychology.

7. Chuck is Richie's older brother, Joanie is Richie's younger sister . . . and don't forget to name Richie (Richard) Cunningham, making three in all.

8. Fonzie went to Milwaukee's Jefferson High but dropped out. Sometime later he re-enrolled, passed a test to prove to himself he could still do it, and dropped out again. Eventually he took night courses and got a diploma along with his friends when they graduated from Jefferson High.

9. Liver

10. The LOVE, AMERICAN STYLE sketch "Love and the Happy Day" starred Ronnie Howard and Anson Williams in 1972 . . . and more directly influenced the shaping of HAPPY DAYS than either GREASE or AMERICAN GRAFFITI.

OLD WHO?

As soon as it was discovered that *all* our Founding Fathers couldn't be called *dad*, a handful of clever people came up with a great many nicknames. The custom continues to this day, though the original nicknamers, one imagines, do not.

Matching Quiz

1. Ethan Allen	*a.* Old Hickory
2. Grover Cleveland	*b.* Father of the Tariff
3. Eugene Field	*c.* Scribe of the Revolution
4. Alexander Hamilton	*d.* Buffalo Hangman
5. Andrew Jackson	*e.* Standard Oil King
6. Thomas Jefferson	*f.* The Poet of Children
7. John D. Rockefeller	*g.* Robin Hood of the Forest
8. Fiorello LaGuardia	*h.* Father of Texas
9. Sam Houston	*i.* Poor Richard
10. Benjamin Franklin	*j.* Little Flower

OLD WHO?

(Answers)

1. *g* . . . because he led a group of forest-based militia called the *Green Mountain Boys* for the good guys during the American Revolution.

2. *d* . . . before he became U.S. President he was sheriff of Erie County with a seat in Buffalo, New York, where he once had to hang a convicted murderer.

3. *f* . . . for his beloved poems about the joys, tears, and wonderment of children.

4. *b* . . . because he set up the U.S. Treasury Department.

5. *a* . . . because his soldiers said he was tough as old hickory wood.

6. *c* . . . for all the many documents of the American Revolution which he write, including the *Declaration of Independence*.

7. *e* . . . because he created and became the first president of Standard Oil Company.

8. *j* . . . a literal translation of the Italian name. *Fiorello* is *little flower*.

9. *h* . . . for his decisive leadership during the key battle of the Texas Revolution, and because he became the first leader of the independent Texas Republic.

10. *i* . . . because he wrote and published *Poor Richard's Almanack*.

WHY SO FORMAL?

Put yourself on a friendlier basis with each of these famous Doctors, Misters, Misses and Missuses by giving their first names.

1. Dr. Jekyll and Mr. Hyde
2. Dr. Kildare
3. Mr. Tibbs
4. Mister Roberts
5. Mr. Skeffington
6. Our Miss Brooks
7. Mr. Magoo
8. Mr. Rogers
9. Mrs. Peel
10. Dr. No

WHY SO FORMAL?

(Answers)

1. Dr. Henry Jekyll and Mr. Edward Hyde
2. Dr. James Kildare
3. Virgil Tibbs
4. Lieutenant Douglas Roberts
5. Job Skeffington
6. Constance ("Connie") Brooks
7. Quincy Magoo
8. Fred Rogers
9. Emma Peel
10. Dr. Julius No

SYNONYM TOAST

Here's a toast to synonyms: Cinnamon toast is tasty and sweet . . . but a synonym toast isn't something to eat.

When you've had a chance to recover from the shock of that tasteless toast, why not take a gander at these ten sets of synonyms—words that sound the same (or almost the same) but have different spellings and meanings.

And unless you're a goose, you won't just take a gander. You'll also tell what they mean . . .

1. disburse / disperse
2. plum / plumb
3. cite / site
4. aisle / isle
5. liable / libel
6. dejure / de jour
7. vain / vein
8. faze / phase
9. eminent / imminent
10. rite / wright

Bonus Stumper: What's the difference between

o! and *oh!*?

SYNONYM TOAST

(Answers)

1. *Disburse* means to pay out funds, as in cash disbursements.
   Disperse means to cause to scatter or separate.

2. *Plum* is the purple fruit. *Plumb* is a lead weight, or something as vertical as if a weight were attached, or downright.

3. *Cite* means to quote or to call upon authoritatively.
   Site is a location.

4. *Aisle* is the passage between theatre seats or church pews.
   Isle is an island.

5. *Liable* means responsible or apt. You can be liable for damages or liable to roll off a log. You can be sued for *libel* if you make damaging remarks about someone in writing.

6. *Dejure* is a legal term meaning "by right." *Du jour* is a French term meaning "of the day," as in soup du jour.

7. *Vain* means fruitless, useless, empty, or unduly prideful.
   Vein is a fissure, a crevice, a streak or a tube that brings blood back to the heart.

8. *Faze* means disconcert or worry. *Phase* means an aspect of something that changes over time.

9. *Eminent* means outstanding. *Imminent* means it's liable to happen immediately.

10. *Rite* is like a ritual. *Wright* is someone who makes something, like a wheelwright.

Bonus Stumper: *O!* is chiefly poetic or used in prayer.
OH! is what you say when you stub your toe or show surprise.

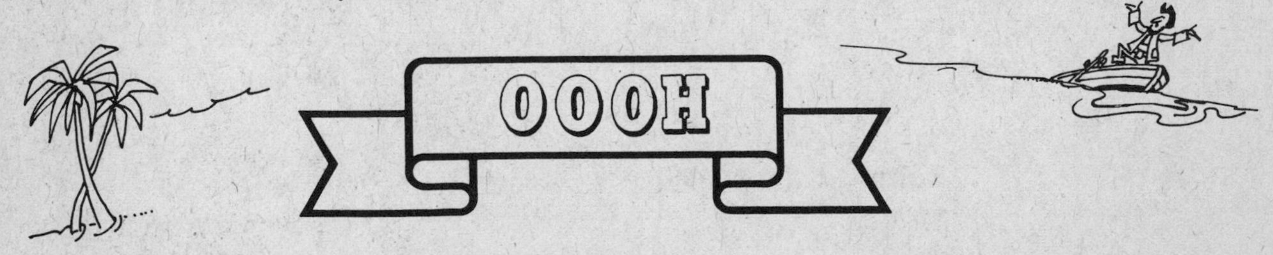

THE REEL ELVIS

How well do you know the movies of The King? Can you answer all ten questions and win a *flaming star* . . . or will you just shrug *that's the way it is* and *spinout*? Incidentally, if you're looking for *double trouble*, you'll find an ELVIS GROOVES quiz later on.

1. TICKLE ME, FOLLOW THAT DOLL, FUN IN ACAPULCO, GIRL HAPPY. Which one isn't an Elvis movie?
2. What was his first movie and what is the name of the character he plays?
3. Which Elvis movie is based on the Harold Robbins bestseller A STONE FOR DANNY FISHER?
4. In which film with a Mid-East setting does he play kidnapped movie star Johnny Tyronne?
5. In one film he plays the dual roles of Josh Morgan and Jodie Tatum. Which one?
6. Who is his sexy co-star in VIVA LAS VEGAS?
7. In which flick does he work for a lady carnival owner played by Barbara Stanwyck?
8. Which of these Elvis films doesn't co-star Shelley Fabares—SPINOUT, CLAMBAKE, GIRL HAPPY, FUN IN ACAPULCO?
9. In which movie does he fall in love with a nun and who plays the nun?
10. Name the back-up group on the soundtrack of ROUSTABOUT.

THE REEL ELVIS

(Answers)

1. FOLLOW THAT DOLL . . . though he did make one called FOLLOW THAT DREAM.

2. LOVE ME TENDER . . . Clint Reno

3. KING CREOLE

4. HARUM SCARUM

5. KISSIN' COUSINS

6. Ann-Margret

7. ROUSTABOUT

8. FUN IN ACAPULCO

9. CHANGE OF HABIT
   . . . Mary Tyler Moore

10. The Jordanaires

RED-LETTER DAZE

What do you call it when you get time off for good behavior—that is, someone else's good behavior?

You call it a commemoration and set your sights on fun, remembering—naturally—exactly what it is you've gotten time off to commemorate. For instance, red-letter days like these . . . .

1. When is Abraham Lincoln's birthday?
2. When is St. Patrick's Day?
3. When is Mother's Day?
4. When is Father's Day?
5. When is Labor Day?
6. What is Memorial Day also called?
7. When is Columbus Day?
8. When is Veterans Day?
9. When is Election Day?
10. When is Flag Day?

RED-LETTER DAZE

(Answers)

1. February 12
2. March 17
3. The second Sunday in May
4. The third Sunday in June
5. The first Monday in September
6. Decoration Day
7. October 12
8. November 11
9. The first Tuesday after the first Monday in November
10. June 14

PIGSKIN PUZZLERS

22-17—Hike! It's time to hit the line. If you fumble you may have to sit on the bench.

1. Who has scored the most points in a career? How many?
2. Who has scored the most touchdowns in a career? How many?
3. Who kicked the longest field goal? How far?
4. Who led the league in rushing thc most years? How many years?
5. Who is the all-time leading rusher?
6. Who has the single-season rushing record? How many yards?
7. Who has completed the most passes in a season? How many?
8. Who has completed the most consecutive passes? How many?
9. Who has the most touchdown passes in a career?
10. Which quarterback passed for the most yards in a single season?

PIGSKIN PUZZLERS

(Answers)

1. George Blanda . . . 2002
2. Jim Brown . . . 126 (106 rushing, 20 passes)
3. Tom Dempsey for New Orleans against Detroit, November 8, 1970, for 68 yards
4. Jim Brown . . . 8 years
5. Jim Brown . . . 12,312 yards
6. O.J. Simpson . . . 2003 (Buffalo, 1973)
7. Dan Fouts completed 360 passes out of 609 attempts for San Diego in 1981
8. Ken Anderson . . . 20 for Cincinnati vs. Houston, January 2, 1983
9. Fran Tarkenton . . . 342
10. Dan Fouts . . . 4802 playing for the San Diego Chargers in 1983

IN THE CARDS

Here's a quiz that any number can play, so if you get stuck, why not find a friend to give you a *hand?* Where can you find such a friend in need? Try the *club*house, or the baseball *diamond*, or just look for someone with plenty of *heart* . . . .

1. How many suits are there in an ordinary deck of cards?

2. What is a deuce? A trey?

3. In 5-card draw poker, what is the highest-ranking hand when playing with a wild card in the deck? Without a wild card?

4. In 5-card draw poker, what is a full house?

5. Which very popular card game is associated with terms like discard pile, meld, knock, gin, and 500?

6. What card game is won by having cards whose numerical value adds up to 21, or comes closer than others to 21 without going over 21?

7. What popular card game has variations such as Klondike, Napoleon at St. Helena, Canfield, and Accordion? (Hint: In the days of the Klondike gold rush, people played *by themselves*).

8. What is the game that involves not only a deck of cards but also a kind of rectangular pegboard with 4 rows of 30 holes each on which players keep score?

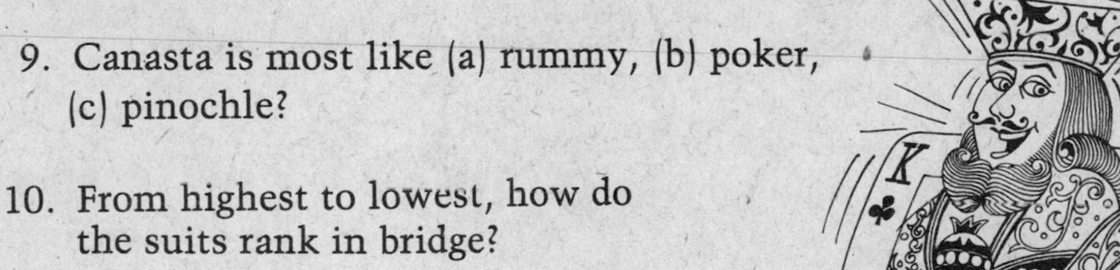

9. Canasta is most like (a) rummy, (b) poker, (c) pinochle?

10. From highest to lowest, how do the suits rank in bridge?

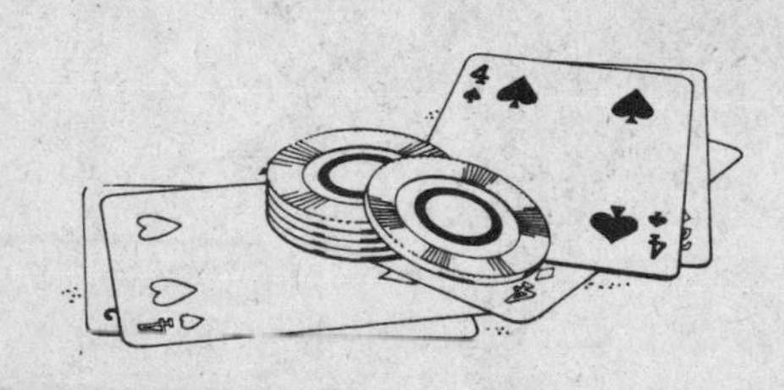

IN THE CARDS

(Answers)

1. Four
2. A two . . . a three
3. Five of a kind . . . a royal flush
4. Three of one kind, a pair of another, for instance three threes and two sevens.
5. Rummy
6. 21 . . . also called Black Jack
7. Solitaire . . . also called Patience
8. Cribbage
9. (a) Rummy
10. Spades, hearts, diamond, clubs

A CARD FRIBBLE

Each king in a deck of playing cards represents a great monarch from history. David is the King of Spades, Alexander the Great is the King of Clubs, Julius Caesar is the King of Diamonds, and Charlemagne is the King of Hearts.

MURDER, SHE SAYS

It's said that Agatha Christie's works have been outstripped in sales only by Shakespeare and the Bible. With 400,000,000 copies in print somewhere on the planet, it's no wonder. But how many of those 400,000,000 have you read?

1. What is Agatha Christie's full name?
2. Who was Mary Westmacott?
3. What Agatha Christie play has been running in London since 1952?
4. Which novel introduces Hercule Poirot?
5. Which novel is considered to be her only "gothic"?
6. Which detective team investigates the disappearance of Old Mrs. Lancaster in BY THE PRICKING OF MY THUMBS?
7. A was for Ascher, B was for Barnard, and there seemed to be 24 more murders on the way in ___________ ?
8. In which Jane Marple tale do we find Elizabeth Temple, Miss Bentham, Emlyn Price and Mr. Casper?
9. Which of these is not a Hercule Poirot case—THE MURDER OF ROGER ACKROYD, THE CLOCKS, MURDER AT THE VICARAGE?
10. Which of these is not a Jane Marple case—HICKORY DICKORY DEATH, A MURDER IS ANNOUNCED, THE TUESDAY CLUB MURDERS?

MURDER, SHE SAYS

(Answers)

1. Dame Agatha Mary Clarissa Miller Christie Mallowan
2. Agatha Christie's pen-name is Mary Westmacott for romantic novels.
3. THE MOUSETRAP
4. THE MYSTERIOUS AFFAIR AT STYLES
5. ENDLESS NIGHT
6. Tommy and Tuppence Beresford
7. THE A.B.C. MURDERS
8. NEMESIS
9. MURDER AT THE VICARAGE
10. HICKORY DICKORY DEATH

CALLING ALL RATS

A popular sign of the day declares: The rat race is over—the rats won.

Where does that leave you in the maze—wandering aimlessly, or each day a little closer to the big cheese? If you're in doubt, you'd better not let the boss catch you doing this quiz on company time . . . .

1. Who wrote THE HIDDEN PERSUADERS, THE STATUS SEEKERS, and THE PYRAMID CLIMBERS?

2. According to #1, the number of Americans who change their address each year is __________ ?

3. Who stars as J.P. Finch in the movie HOW TO SUCCEED IN BUSINESS WITHOUT REALLY TRYING?

4. To which company does #3 rise to the very top?

5. Who stars as THE MAN IN THE WHITE SUIT in the 1952 British movie?

6. Gregory Peck and Jennifer Jones star in what movie about the Madison Avenue rat race?

7. Says David Merrick, "It's not enough that I should succeed—others __________ __________ ."

8. Says Paul Goodman, "Few great men could pass __________ ."

9. Margaret Mead once said, "Sooner or later I'm going to die but __________ __________ __________ __________ __________ ."

10. According to Lily Tomlin, "The trouble with the rat race is that even if you win, __________ __________ __________ __________ ."

CALLING ALL RATS

(Answers)

1. Vance Packard
2. 40 million
3. Robert Morse
4. Worldwide Wicket Company
5. Alec Guinness
6. THE MAN IN THE GRAY FLANNEL SUIT
7. ". . . should fail."
8. ". . . Personnel."
9. ". . . I'm not going to retire."
10. ". . . you're still a rat."

THAR SHE BLOWS

Some sixty million years ago—so the story goes—hairy, four-legged mammals took to the seas for food or safety, and in a mere matter of eons, turned into whales. Just think of all the trivia that's piled up since then!

1. What is the largest mammal in the history of the world?
2. True or false—in infancy, #1 can grow as much as 100 pounds a day?
3. Which whale has a long, spiraled tusk like a unicorn?
4. Do whales have teeth?
5. What is the IWC?
6. Who wrote MOBY DICK?
7. In which Walt Disney movie do we find the song "A Whale of a Tale"?
8. What is the name of the whale that swallows Pinocchio?
9. What is the background music of Judy Collins' "Farewell to Tarwathie"?
10. Name the director of the classic versions of FRANKENSTEIN, BRIDE OF FRANKENSTEIN, and SHOWBOAT.

THAR SHE BLOWS

(Answers)

1. The blue whale

2. True—in fact, as much as 200!

3. The narwhal

4. Some 65 species do, the rest don't.

5. The International Whaling Commission gathers information about whales, sets kill quotas, and conserves endangered species.

6. Herman Melville

7. 20,000 LEAGUES UNDER THE SEA

8. Monstro

9. Actual recordings of the "Songs of the Humpback Whale"

10. James Whale

UP, UP AND AWAY

Look—halfway between the moon and your basement! What do you see? Volcanic ash? UFOs? Bat Imp?

Whatever you see, you're so cool it doesn't bother you. Right? Terrific. So don't go into a tailspin when you see these questions about denizens of the wild blue yonder . . .

1. What was new around Kitty Hawk on December 17, 1903?
2. What was the name of Lindbergh's plane for his historic solo New York-to-Paris flight of May 21, 1927?
3. Translate *Luftwaffe*. Also, what was it?
4. What airline advertises "friendly skies"?
5. On the TV series SKY KING, what was the name of the ranch?
6. What was the name of Sky King's niece?
7. What was the name of the Ken Tobey TV series about a helicopter charter service?
8. In which Astaire-Rogers movie do showgirls do a club act strapped to the wings of planes?
9. Where is the U.S. Air Force Academy?
10. What Lancaster- Kerr-Hackman movie concerns skydivers in Kansas?

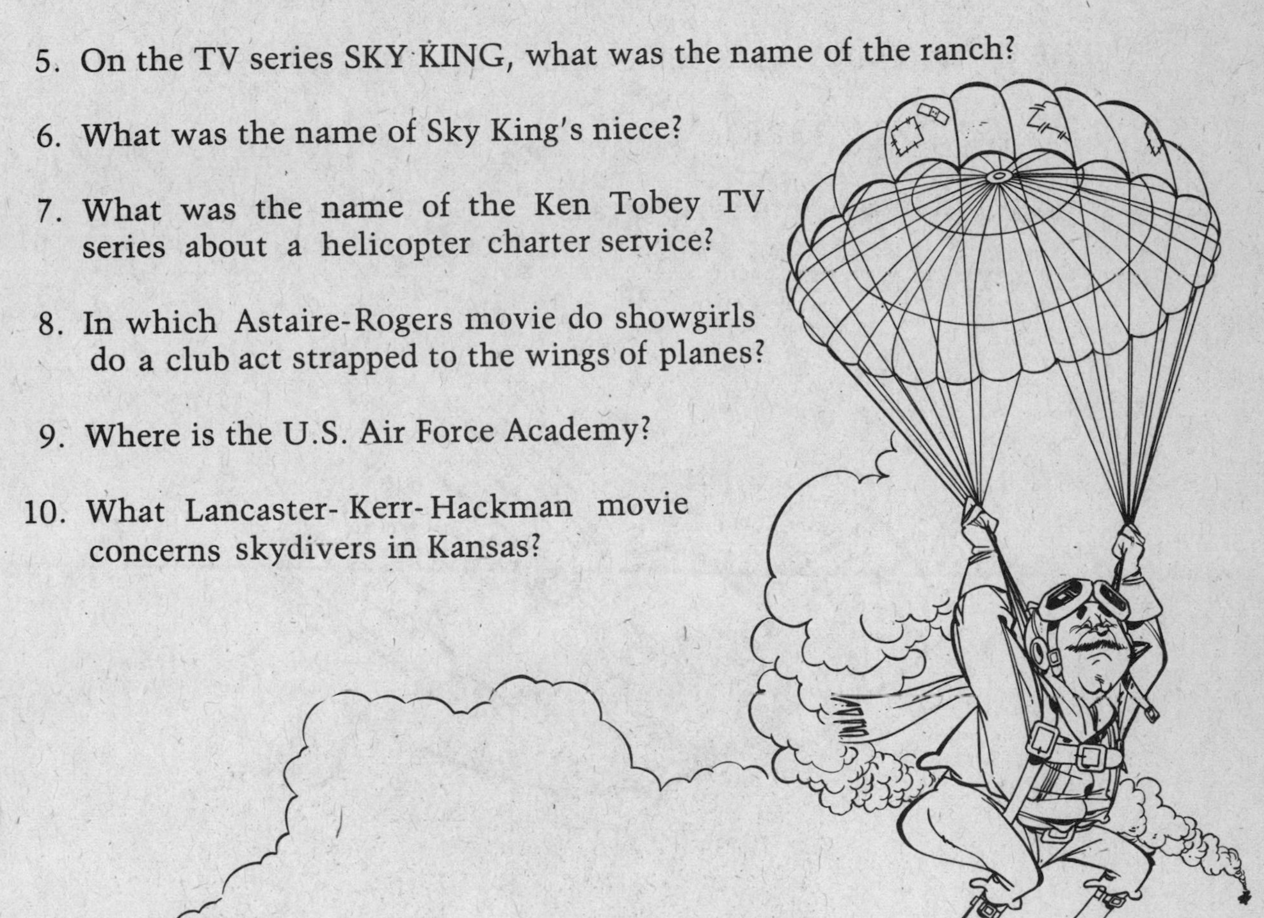

UP, UP AND AWAY

(Answers)

1. The Wright Brothers Wilbur and Orville made the first controlled, sustained flights in a power-driven, heavier-than-air-machine at Kill Devils Hill, near Kitty Hawk, North Carolina. Of the four flights made that day, the first lasted 12 seconds the the fourth lasted a big 59 seconds.
2. The Spirit of St. Louis
3. Air weapon . . . the air force of the Third Reich
4. United Air Lines
5. The Flying Crown Ranch
6. Penny (Gloria Winters)
7. THE WHIRLYBIRDS (sometimes known as COPTER PATROL)
8. FLYING DOWN TO RIO
9. North of Colorado Springs, Colorado
10. THE GYPSY MOTHS

OH, BABY!

If it's pink and little and goes *waaaa*, chances are it's a baby. But if you have any doubts, you can always ask the stork. *She* scored 100% on this bouncing bundle of bafflement!

1. In the movie BRINGING UP BABY, what was "Baby"?

2. What song celebrates the joys of Molly and me and baby (makes three)?

3. Complete the following: "A baby is God's opinion that __________."

4. Complete this Ronald Arbuthnot Knox definition of a baby: "A loud noise at one end and __________."

5. Who played Baby Jane Hudson in WHAT EVER HAPPENED TO BABY JANE? Who played her sister?

6. Name the Yvonne Lime - Ronnie Burns TV show about a baby who talked—not to them but to us, the audience.

7. Who played BACHELOR MOTHER in the 1939 film of the same name?

8. Who played the same role in the remake, and what was it called?

9. What was the nickname of a crook named Nelson who belonged to John Dillinger's gang?

10. Right after THE WIZARD OF OZ, Judy Garland made a film with Mickey Rooney—about the kids of show folk putting on a show of their own. What was it called? Who wrote the music?

OH, BABY!

(Answers)

1. A pet leopard
2. "My Blue Heaven"
3. ". . . the world should go on." (Carl Sandburg)
4. ". . . no sense of responsibility at the other."
5. Bette Davis . . . Joan Crawford
6. HAPPY
7. Ginger Rogers
8. Debbie Reynolds . . . BUNDLE OF JOY
9. "Baby Face"
10. BABES IN ARMS . . . Rodgers and Hart

Unless you have more than your fill of bills, you may have a little trouble identifying all of these bill-filling faces. On the other hand, think how you can impress people once you've mastered this portrait gallery of golden grins!

1. Whose portrait appears on both versions of the $2 bill?
2. What scene is on the back of the Bicentennial $2 bill?
3. Whose portrait is on the $20 bill?
4. Whose portrait is on the $50 bill?
5. Whose portrait is on the $100 bill?
6. On the $500?
7. On the $1000?
8. On the $5000?
9. What became of bills for $500 and up after 1969?
10. What is the designated use of the $100,000 bill?

ILLING TH BILL

(Answers)

1. Thomas Jefferson
2. The Signing of the Declaration of Independence
3. Andrew Jackson
4. Ulysses Simpson Grant
5. Benjamin Franklin
6. William McKinley
7. Grover Cleveland
8. James Madison
9. They were discontiniued.
10. Transactions between the Federal Reserve System and the U.S. Treasury Department

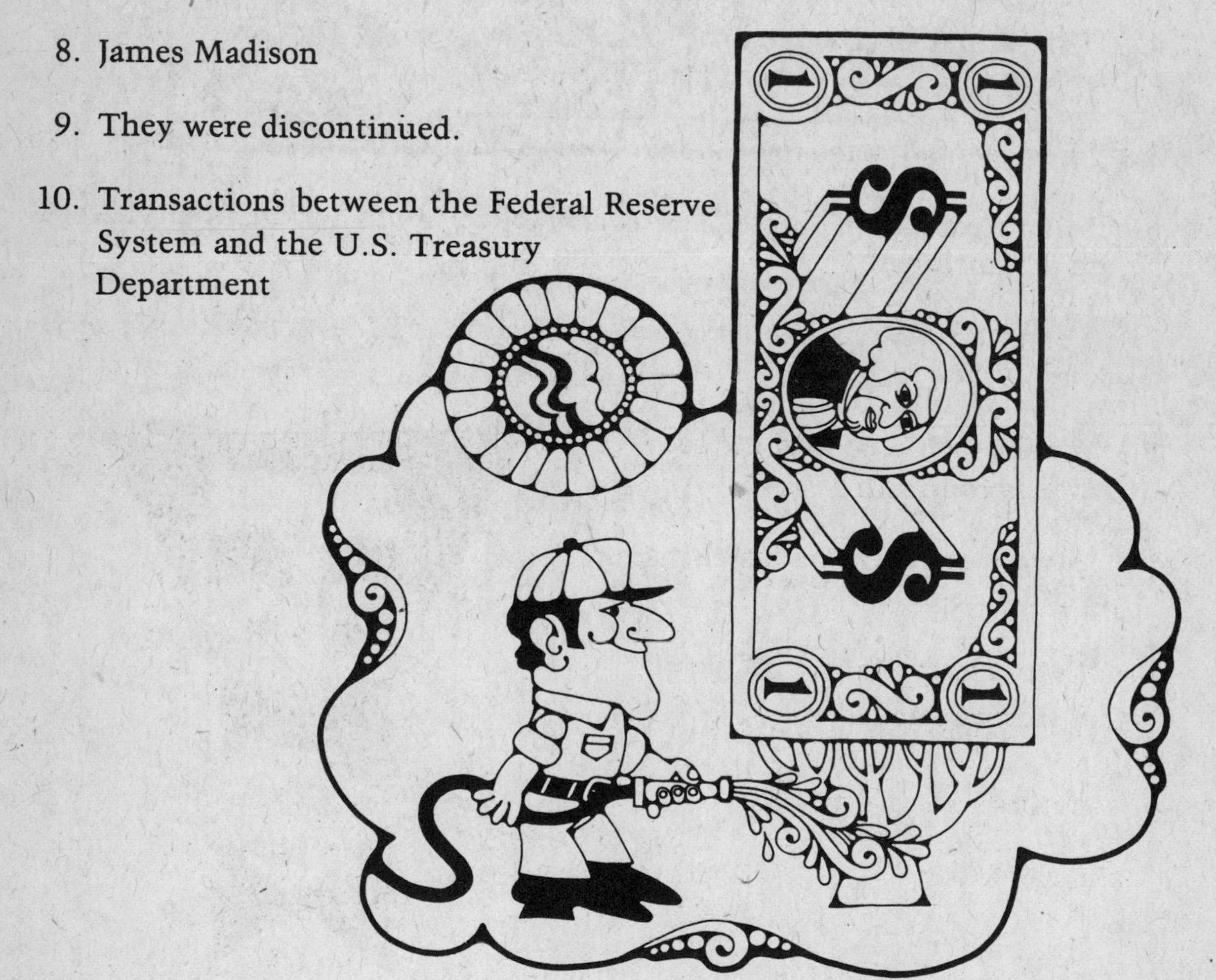

SAY IT AGAIN, SUPERSTAR!

Some celebrities are not only true to their words but known for them as well. Here are a handful of cases in point. Do you know who said—

1. "Give me a couple of pages of the Bible and I'll give you a picture."
2. "A wide screen makes a bad film twice as bad."
3. "The public has always expected me to be a playboy, and a decent chap never lets his public down."
4. "This King stuff is pure bull . . . . I'm just a lucky slob from Ohio who happened to be in the right place at the right time."
5. "I never said, I want to be alone. I only said I want to be let alone."
6. "I don't care to belong to any social organization which would accept me as a member."
7. "Television is a medium, so called because it is neither rare nor well done."
8. "A man should control his life. Mine is controlling me."
9. "Always make the audience suffer as much as possible."
10. "I was a fourteen-year-old boy for thirty years."

SAY IT AGAIN, SUPERSTAR!

(Answers)

1. Cecil B. de Mille
2. Sam Goldwyn
3. Errol Flynn
4. Clark Gable
5. Greta Garbo
6. Groucho Marx
7. Ernie Kovacs
8. Rudolph Valentino
9. Alfred Hitchcock
10. Mickey Rooney

AROUND THE WORLD IN 80 FLICKS— SECOND LEG

What's the matter? Jet lag so soon? Well, you'd better catch your breath and get to work on this second leg of our round-the-world-with-movies matching quiz. Don't forget, you haven't finished *this* journey till you've found and solved all 8 quizzes—and answered 80 questions in all!

1. THE MISFITS	a. Bronx
2. THE CRAWLING EYE	b. New Guinea
3. THE GUNS OF NAVARONE	c. Burmese jungle
4. TO BE OR NOT TO BE	d. Swiss Alps
5. SKULLDUGGERY	e. Warsaw
6. HOW GREEN WAS MY VALLEY	f. Amazon jungle
7. THE WANDERERS	g. Reno
8. JIVARO	h. Aegean Sea
9. MERRILL'S MARAUDERS	i. Wales
10. THE NIGHT OF THE GRIZZLY	j. Wyoming

Answers: 1 *g*, 2 *d*, 3 *h*, 4 *e*, 5 *b*, 6 *i*, 7 *a*, 8 *f*, 9 *c*, 10 *j*.

HAR-DE-HAR-HAR-HAR

Return to us now to those thrilling days on Chauncey Street, Brooklyn, U.S.A., where Ralph and Alice Kramden take turns scrapping and making up, in THE HONEYMOONERS . . . .

1. Where does Ralph work?
2. Who are his closest friends and upstairs neighbors?
3. Where does Norton work?
4. What was Alice's maiden name?
5. What kind of refrigerator do the Kramdens have?
6. What's the name of Ralph's lodge?
7. Where is the Raccoon National Cemetery?
8. "Can it core a apple?" refers to what Kramden scheme?
9. What's the name of the Kramdens' and Nortons' favorite Chinese restaurant?
10. What is the song that Ralph *can't* identify when he's a contestant on THE 99,000 ANSWER?

HAR-DE-HAR-HAR-HAR

(Answers)

1. Ralph works for New York's (mythical) Gotham Bus Company.
2. Ed and Trixie Norton
3. Ed works in the New York sewers.
4. Gibson
5. They don't have a refrigerator. They have an ice box.
6. The International Order of Friendly Raccoons (or sometimes, The Royal Order of Raccoons)
7. Bismarck, North Dakota
8. When Ralph and Ed try to sell Handy Housewife Helpers on TV, Ed dresses as the Chef of the Past and asks Ralph, dressed as the Chef of the Future, ''can it core a apple''?
9. The Hong Kong Gardens
10. ''Swanee River''

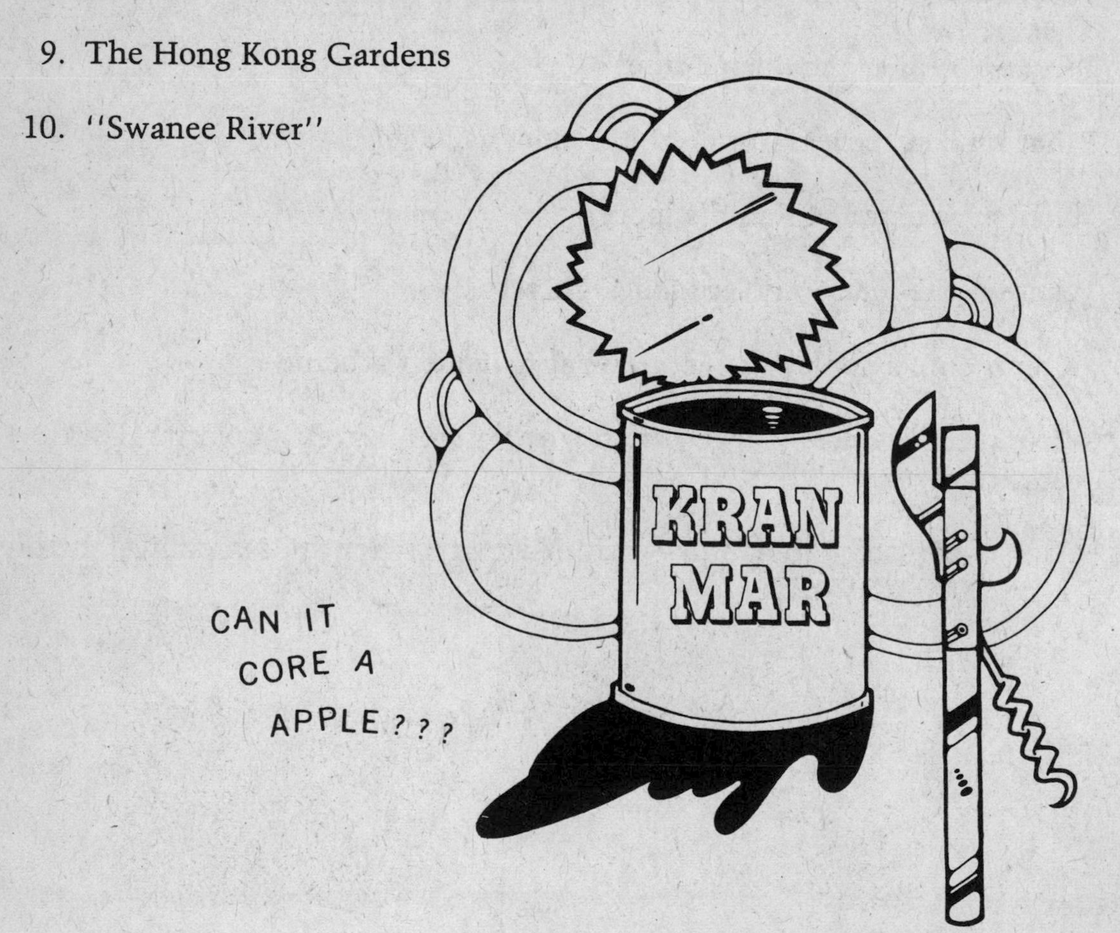

CHECKMATE

It's been said that chess is the oldest game of pure mental skill in which there's no element of chance whatever. But whoever said it apparently never heard of trivia. Boy oh boy, has somebody been rooked!

1. With what Persian word did the word *chess* originate?
2. What word do we get from *shah mat*?
3. With how many pieces does each chess player begin?
4. How many squares are on a chess board?
5. Which piece moves in an L-shape?
6. Which player has the first move?
7. What are ranks?
8. What are files?
9. What is meant by the notation QB?
10. What is meant by *x* in chess notation?

CHECKMATE

(Answers)

1. *Shah* (king)
2. Checkmate . . . *shah mat* means ''the king is dead''
3. 16
4. 64
5. Knight
6. White
7. A line of squares moving left-to-right on a board
8. A line of squares directly in front of a piece
9. Queen's bishop, or the bishop on the queen's side
10. *x* designates a capture.

THE HOSTS WITH THE MOST

If you know your TV game shows, it should be a snap for you to name the happy-go-lucky hosts who emcee each of these go-for-the-bundle giveaways. Of course, if you're really gone on game shows, you may think you should win money for getting these answers.

Are you always so gullible?

1. THE GONG SHOW
2. LET'S MAKE A DEAL
3. THE DATING GAME
4. HOLLYWOOD SQUARES
5. $20,000 PYRAMID
6. $64,000 QUESTION
7. FAMILY FEUD
8. PASSWORD PLUS
9. QUEEN FOR A DAY
10. MATCH GAME

THE HOSTS WITH THE MOST

(Answers)

1. Chuck Barris
2. Monty Hall
3. Jim Lang
4. Peter Marshall
5. Dick Clark
6. Hal March
7. Richard Dawson
8. Allen Ludden
9. Jack Bailey
10. Gene Rayburn

MONSTERS OF THE DEEP

How real are sea monsters? Ask Thor Heyerdahl—he spent several hours eyeball-to-jaws with what may have been the biggest fish ever seen by man. But you might want to start your search for sea-going dragons on a slightly smaller scale, for instance, with this quiz . . . .

1. In KON-TIKI, Thor Heyerdahl describes his meeting with a whale shark at sea. Its jaws were between four and five feet wide. Where was he when he saw it?
2. According to the Navy-Smithsonian Shark Attack File, which species of shark is most dangerous?
3. Scientists believe the shark was the first animal to develop __________ ?
4. What oddly-shaped sea creature has injured more people than all other fish combined?
5. Which two aquatic animals are perilous to humans because of the electrical charges they can deliver when provoked?
6. Which river-dwelling fish of South America can skeletonize a horse within a few minutes?
7. What is the chief weapon of the scorpion fish?
8. How many arms does an octopus have?
9. What marine organism, sometimes called the deadliest creature alive, has a poisoning ability greater than any snake?
10. What name is given to the prehistoric aquatic creature that is occasionally reported swimming in a lake in Scotland?

MONSTERS OF THE DEEP

(Answers)

1. He and his crew of five were on a small balsa-wood raft.

2. The great white shark

3. Teeth

4. The ray

5. Electric rays and electric eels

6. The piranha

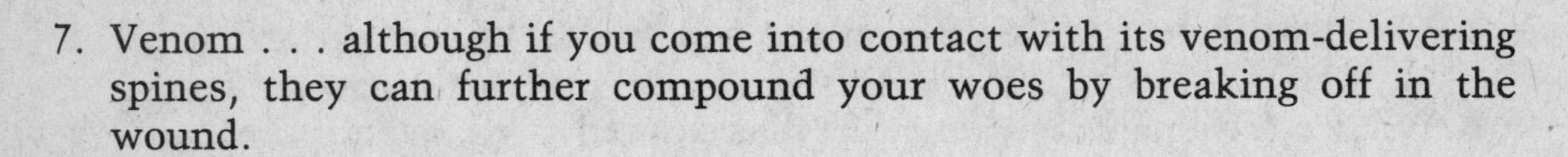

7. Venom . . . although if you come into contact with its venom-delivering spines, they can further compound your woes by breaking off in the wound.

8. Eight

9. The sea wasp, a sort of jellyfish

10. The Loch Ness Monster or sometimes just Nessie

TEEN TALES

From bobbysox to beatniks to bikini beach and beyond, movies, books and TV shows for and about the teen set have never been out of style—even though what's *in* style has never stopped changing.

To test your TTQ (teen-trivia quotient), bebop up to these ten questions. They're swell . . . uh, keen-o . . . uh, groovy uh . . . bad?

1. What are the names of the Hardy Boys?
2. Who played Maynard G. Krebs in TV's THE MANY LOVES OF DOBIE GILLIS?
3. Who played Dobie and his favorite sweetie, Thalia Menninger, in #2?
4. What did Andy Hardy's daddy do for a living?
5. In what TV series did Patty Duke play a double role?
6. Who became one of the top symbols of the "lost 50s" with movies like REBEL WITHOUT A CAUSE?
7. In which 1954 film does Marlon Brando star as the leader of a motorcycle gang?
8. What was Pat Boone's first film?
9. Who was Paramount's first Henry Aldrich? Who is most often identified with the role?
10. FIREBALL . . . BIKINI BEACH . . . BIKINI WEDDING . . . THE MONKEY'S UNCLE—which is not an Annette Funicello film?

TEEN TALES

(Answers)

1. Joe and Frank
2. Bob Denver
3. Dwayne Hickman . . . Tuesday Weld
4. Judge Hardy was a judge
5. THE PATTY DUKE SHOW . . . as identical cousins Patty and Cathy
6. James Dean
7. THE WILD ONE
8. BERNADINE
9. Jackie Cooper . . . Jimmy Lydon
10. BIKINI WEDDING

FRIBBLE

James Dean may be the all-time symbol of restless youth, yet the fact is, he was not a teenager but in his early twenties when he made his first important films, EAST OF EDEN and REBEL WITHOUT A CAUSE, in 1955. Tragically, this was also the year of his death.

CURTAIN CALLS!

Closing lines—bad plays need good ones or they're merely interminable. Great plays need better ones or they just not immortal.

Whether *these* closing lines stand the test of time, only time will tell. But whether you pass this test of guessing the plays they come from is entirely up to you!

1. "Trapped . . . but happy . . . which isn't too bad for the end of a musical comedy. Ta da!"
2. "Captain, this is Ensign Pulver. I just threw your palm trees overboard. Now what's all this crap about no movie tonight?"
3. "Then let's play poker. And watch your cigarettes, will ya? This is my house, not a pig sty."
4. "Yeah, I'm all choked up."
5. "Eliza? Where the devil are my slippers?"
6. "Run, boy!"

CURTAIN CALLS!

(Answers)

1. PIPPIN
2. MISTER ROBERTS
3. THE ODD COUPLE
4. GREASE
5. MY FAIR LADY
6. CAMELOT

MOONMEN

The song says it's only a paper moon but that's pure hogwash because everyone knows the astronauts came back with all kinds of rocks and not a single lunar gum wrapper.

Of course, it's only a few steps to colonization. And after that, moongum wrappers may be only a matter of time . . . .

1. Which is closer, the moon or the sun?
2. What does *CM* stand for? What does *LM* stand for?
3. Although *CM* pilots didn't actually touch the moon, what unique distinction do they share?
4. To escape the pull of Earth's gravity, astronauts were accelerated to a speed eleven times faster than a rifle bullet or (a) 24,000 mph, (b) 48,000 mph, (c) 64,000 mph?
5. Name the three astronauts of the first manned landing on the moon.
6. What was the name and number of the mission described in #5? What was the date of the landing?
7. The astronauts in #5 landed on the moon's Sea of ___________ ?
8. How many U.S. Apollo moon missions have there been?
9. Who was the first American spaceman? Was he ever on the moon?
10. In all, how many American astronauts have gone to the moon?

MOONMEN

(Answers)

1. The moon

2. Command-module . . . Lunar-module

3. *CM* pilots are the only men of the Apollo missions who were entirely alone in space. While their Apollo crewmen went to the moon's surface, the *CM* pilots were circling the light and even the *dark side* of the moon!

4. (a) 24,000 mph

5. Neil A. Armstrong, Edwin E. Aldrin, Jr., Michael Collins

6. Apollo 11 . . . July 20, 1969

7. Tranquillity

8. Eleven—Apollo 7 through Apollo 17

9. Alan B. Shepard, Jr. . . . who was also on the team of Apollo 14, the third manned lunar landing.

10. Twenty-four

UNCOMMON YET IN COMMON

These folks may have nothing in common with you but it's sure they have an uncommon something in common with each other. Remember the old joke—what did Abraham Lincoln and Calvin Coolidge have in common? (They both had beards except Coolidge.)

Well, forget it and get serious! You'll have to put on your thinking cap for this one.

1. What do Bobby Sherman, David Soul and Robert Brown have in common?
2. John Weissmuller, Ethel Lackie, Martha Norelius?
3. Boris Spassky, Bobby Fischer, Mikhail Botvinnik?
4. Bloomers, leotards, guillotines?
5. Calamity Jane, Marie MacDonald, Elizabeth Taylor, Zsa Zsa Gabor?
6. Emily Dickinson, Lizzie Borden, Rhonda Fleming, Jeanette MacDonald?
7. Victoria Woodhull, Ann Milburn, Charlene Mitchell?
8. Sir Barton, Whirlaway, Count Fleet, Citation, Secretariat?
9. Ann-Margret, Ingrid Bergman, Greta Garbo?
10. Ava Gardner, Mia Farrow, Nancy Barbato?

UNCOMMON YET IN COMMON

(Answers)

1. They were the Bolt brothers in the TV series HERE COME THE BRIDES.

2. All three won Olympic medals for swimming for the U.S. in 1924.

3. All three have won the World Championship of Chess.

4. All three are named after the people who first popularized them—Amelia Bloomer (feminist), Jules Leotard (aerialist), Louisette Guillotine (physician).

5. They've all been married at least 5 times—Calamity Jane holding the record (so far) with 10 husbands.

6. They're all redheads.

7. All three women ran for President of the United States.

8. All five horses are U.S. Triple Crown winners.

9. All three were born in Stockholm, Sweden.

10. All three have been married to Frank Sinatra.

ABOUT TIME

Are you time-wise? Always late? Always early? Always punctual to a fault? Whatever your answer, don't blame yourself (your friends will do that for you!)

And by all means, don't use a stopwatch for this quiz about time—unless you're the all-time glutton for punishment.

1. Who founded *Time* magazine?
2. What was H.G. Wells' first novel?
3. Name Manhattan's controversial catch-all on the corners of Broadway and 42nd Street.
4. What were U.S. militia men called during the Revolutionary War?
5. In 1776, patriot Thomas Paine wrote in COMMON SENSE that "these are the times that __________ __________ __________"?
6. Name Jack Benny's much-maligned movie about the angel come to earth to destroy it with a toot of his horn.
7. What happens at Cafe Mozart, 8 o'clock?
8. What ordinary objects are usually never installed in gambling casinos?
9. Name the Spencer Tracy - Frank Sinatra movie about a priest, a children's hospital, and a volcano.
10. What vintage movie concludes with a dinner attended by Marie Dressler, John Barrymore, Jean Harlow, Lionel Barrymore and others?

ABOUT TIME

(Answers)

1. Henry R. Luce and Briton Hadden
2. THE TIME MACHINE
3. Times Square
4. Minutemen
5. ". . . try men's souls."
6. THE HORN BLOWS AT MIDNIGHT
7. Holly Martin betrays Harry Lime in THE THIRD MAN.
8. Clocks
9. THE DEVIL AT 4 O'CLOCK
10. DINNER AT EIGHT

GRIDIRON

If you have the *stomach* for football, try your *hand* at these *brain* bruisers by putting your *toe* in. Now go a *head* . . .

GROANERS

1. Who won the 1980 Heisman Trophy Award and for what team did he play?
2. Which two teams competed in the first Super Bowl and what was the outcome?
3. What quarterback has passed for the most yards in a career and how many?
4. Who has the most total yards gained in a lifetime and how many?
5. Who has the most total yards gained in a season? How many?
6. What is the longest pass interception return and who holds this record?
7. Who holds the record for most field goals in a single game? How many?
8. Who holds the records for touchdowns in a season?
9. Who has played in the most seasons and how many?
10. Who holds the record for touchdowns rushing in a season? How many?

GRIDIRON GROANERS

(Answers)

1. Charles White, who was the leading rusher with 1,803 yards on 293 carries with an average of 6.2 yards per carry and 180.3 yards per game while playing for USC.

2. Green Bay Packers and Kansas City Chiefs. Green Bay won 35-10.

3. Fran Tarkenton with 47,003

4. Jim Brown . . . 15,459 yards

5. Terry Metcalf . . . 2,462 yards (1975)

6. 102 yards for a touchdown . . . Bob Smith, Detroit against Chicago, November 24, 1949

7. Jim Bakken for St. Louis against Pittsburgh . . . 7 (September 24, 1967)

8. O.J. Simpson, Buffalo Bills (1975) . . . 16 running, 7 on passes

9. George Blanda . . . 26 (1949-1975)

10. Jim Taylor . . . 19 T.D.'s (Green Bay, 1962)
    Earl Campbell . . . 19 T.D.'s (Houston, 1979)
    Chuck Munice . . . 19 T.D.'s (San Diego, 1981)

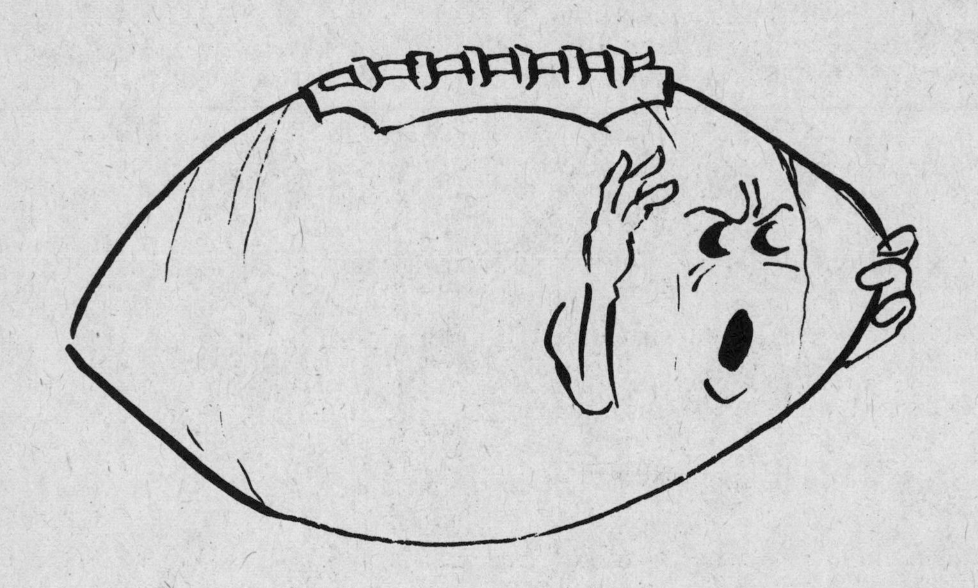

DOWN MEDLEY LANE

You know what it is when someone sings a few bars of one song, then a snatch of another, then doodle-doodle-dee from yet a third, and so on, don't you?

Of course you do. It's an infernal nuisance!

But it's also a medley, which brings us to the point of this quiz which asks the musical question—to which 10 Broadway shows would a songster be paying tribute by singing these 10 sets of songs?

1. "Shall We Dance?", "I Whistle a Happy Tune," "I Have Dreamed"?
2. "Wunderbar," "Why Can't You Behave?", "Brush Up Your Shakespeare"?
3. "I Love Paris," "C'est Magnifique," "Allez-vous en"?
4. "Marian the Librarian," "Shipoopi," "Till There Was You"?
5. "Some Enchanted Evening," "Bloody Mary," "Happy Talk"?
6. "One Kiss," "Stouthearted Men," "Lover, Come Back to Me"?
7. "Hey There," "Steam Heat," "Hernando's Hideaway"?
8. "People Will Say We're In Love," "Kansas City," "All er Nothin'"?
9. "Tea for Two," "I Want to Be Happy," "Telephone Girlie"?

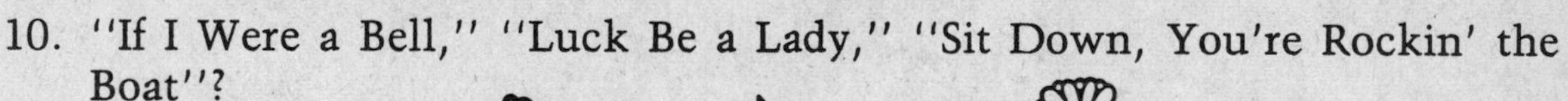

10. "If I Were a Bell," "Luck Be a Lady," "Sit Down, You're Rockin' the Boat"?

DOWN MEDLEY LANE

(Answers)

1. THE KING AND I
2. KISS ME KATE
3. CAN-CAN
4. THE MUSIC MAN
5. SOUTH PACIFIC
6. THE NEW MOON

7. THE PAJAMA GAME
8. OKLAHOMA!
9. NO, NO, NANETTE
10. GUYS AND DOLLS

GREAT DATES

All great dates don't necessarily involve going out with someone and having a great time. Some of the greatest dates ever are those on which important ideas, events, or people are remembered.

So it stands to reason that the greatest possible date is—what else?—when you go out with someone for the express purpose of doing this quiz about calendar dates you surely don't want to forget . . .

1. What does Memorial (or Decoration) Day commemorate?
2. What does Armistice (or Veterans) Day commemorate?
3. What does Columbus Day commemorate?
4. When is American Indian Day?
5. When is Pan American Day?
6. When is Poetry Day?
7. When is U.N. Day?
8. When is Bill of Rights Day?
9. When is Groundhog Day?
10. What is the significance of Groundhog Day?

GREAT DATES

(Answers)

1. Originally honoring only the Civil War dead, Memorial or Decoration Day now honors all who died in the military and naval service of the U.S.

2. Originally commemorating the signing of the Armistice ending World War I, Armistice or Veterans Day recognizes all who have served in the American armed forces.

3. The discovery of America by Columbus in 1492—more specifically, the day he first sighted the islands of the New World.

4. The fourth Friday in September

5. April 14

6. October 15

7. October 24

8. December 15

9. February 2

10. Legend says that if the groundhog comes out of his hole on February 2 and sees his shadow, he returns to his burrow and there'll be six more weeks of winter.

WHODUNIT?

Everybody loves a mystery. Particularly when it comes to the all-important *who*, as in who done it, who got it, and in this case, who created . . . .

1. Nick Charles?
2. Philo Vance?
3. Charlie Chan?
4. Perry Mason?
5. Nero Wolfe?
6. Mr. Moto?
7. Philip Marlowe?
8. Inspector Maigret?
9. Lewis A. Archer?
10. Lord Peter Wimsey?

FRIBBLE

For the Fiftieth Anniversary of INTERPOL, Nicaragua issued a series of stamps commemorating Famous Fictional Detectives. Representing Perry Mason is—who else—Raymond Burr. Burr, as it happens, is an avid stamp collector.

WHODUNIT?

(Answers)

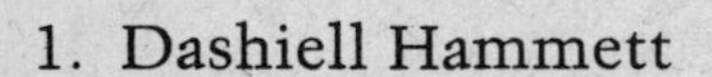

1. Dashiell Hammett
2. S.S. Van Dine
3. Earl Derr Biggers
4. Erle Stanley Gardner
5. Rex Stout
6. John P. Marquand
7. Raymond Chandler
8. Georges Simenon
9. Ross Macdonald
10. Dorothy L. Sayers

THE QUOTABLE FRANKLIN

Everybody knows what Ben Franklin said, even if they don't know he said it. Everybody? Well, we'll soon find out . . .

1. What is time?

2. There never was a good war or _______ _______ __________ ?

3. Whom does God help?

4. What makes a man healthy, wealthy, and wise?

5. What does he say will happen to the signers of the Declaration of Independence if they don't hang together?

6. Here lies Skugg—how?

7. The heart of the fool is in his mouth—but where is the mouth of the wise man?

8. What are the only things certain in this world?

9. What is the stuff life is made of?

10. What's the 8th and last reason for preferring older women as romantic partners?

THE QUOTABLE FRANKLIN

(answers)

1. "Remember that time is money."
2. ". . . a bad peace."
3. "God helps them that help themselves."
4. "Early to bed and early to rise."
5. ". . . assuredly we shall all hang separately."
6. ". . . snug as a bug in a rug."
7. ". . . in his heart."
8. ". . . death and taxes."
9. "Then do not squander time,
   for that is the stuff life is made of."
10. "They are so grateful."

NURSERY RHYME TIME

Ding, dong, bell . . . do you know them well?
If you don't know your nursery rhymes . . . this quiz will surely tell.

1. How much are hot cross buns?
2. How many wives had the man on the road to St. Ives?
3. Goosey, Goosey gander, whither shall I wander?
4. How did the man in the moon burn his mouth on the way to Norwich?
5. Why would anybody want to ride a cock-horse to Banbury Cross?
6. Complete this jingle—Tinker, Tailor, Soldier, Sailor, ___________, ___________, ___________, ___________, ___________, ___________.
7. Who killed Cock Robin?
8. Who saw him die?
9. What are little boys made of?
10. After sticking his thumb in his Christmas pie and pulling it out with plum goo all over it, what unlikely conclusion did Little Jack Horner draw?

NURSERY RHYME TIME

(answers)

1. One a penny, two a penny

2. Seven

3. Upstairs and downstairs and in my lady's chamber

4. Supping cold plum porridge

5. To see a fine lady upon a white horse . . . rings on her fingers and bells on her toes . . . and she shall have music wherever she goes.

6. Rich man, Poor man, Beggarman, Thief

7. I, said the Sparrow

8. I, said the Fly

9. Frogs and snails and puppy dogs' tails

10. What a good boy am I!

LET'S HORSE AROUND

All these answers include the word *horse*—and most have absolutely nothing else to do with horses. But don't be disappointed, horse fans, your turn will come!

1. Marx Brothers movie about a college football game.

2. Ally of Sitting Bull.

3. A long drink made of gingerale and brandy or whiskey.

4. A brassicaceous herb of which the root is used for a condiment.

5. Ichabod Crane's pursuer in THE LEGEND OF SLEEPY HOLLOW.

6. What Richard III says on Bosworth Field in the Shakespeare play.

7. War, pestilence, famine and death in the Revelation of St. John in the Bible.

8. The ruse by which the Greeks put an end to the siege of Troy.

9. A John Wayne-William Holden movie about Yankees in the South during the Civil War.

10. According to Abraham Lincoln, what the old Dutch farmer said to his companion.

LET'S HORSE AROUND

(answers)

1. HORSE FEATHERS

2. Crazy Horse

3. Horse's Neck

4. Horseradish

5. The Headless Horseman

6. "A horse! a horse! my kingdom for a horse!"

7. The Four Horsemen of the Apocalypse

8. The Trojan Horse

9. THE HORSE SOLDIERS

10. "It was not best to swap horses in mid-stream."

STRICTLY STONE AGE

What's wrong with this picture?

That's Victor Mature down there in ONE MILLION B.C. and the fact is men like that and dinosaurs like that didn't fight like that in one million B.C. But you can't blame Hollywood. After all, who wants to see a movie about the real stone age—featuring a cave-man chipping a tool out of stone?

1. Who starred in the remake of ONE MILLION B.C.?

2. What does *prehistoric* mean? *Primordial*?

3. What does a paleontologist study? An anthropologist?

4. For what are Altamira and Lascaux famous?

5. What dinosaur had a name that means Tyrant King?

6. What was the background music for the dinosaur sequence in Walt Disney's FANTASIA?

7. What was the Piltdown hoax?

8. What is the name of Johnny Hart's stone-age comic strip?

9. What comic strip character rides his pet dinosaur Dinny through King Guzzle's Kingdom of Moo?

10. Ringo Starr dons animal skins for a campy stone-age movie called ___________ ?

STRICTLY STONE AGE

(answers)

1. Raquel Welch and John Richardson

2. Before history could be recorded, in other words, before writing . . . first created, or first in a particular order, which is as early as you can get.

3. Animal fossils . . . the origin, culture, characteristics and distribution of the human race.

4. Cave paintings left by Cro-Magnon man.

5. Tyrannosaurus rex

6. "The Rite of Spring" by Igor Stravinsky

7. A scientist "discovered" and assembled what was believed to be the fossil remnants of the skull of the missing link, and it took 40 years for the world to learn that it was really the skull of a modern man paired with the jaw bone of a modern ape. People who went to school in the first half of this century still may not know it's a hoax. If you know any people like that, break it to them gently.

8. B.C.

9. Alley Oop

10. CAVEMAN

APRIL FOOLS

April comes from the Latin *aperire,* meaning "to open," because all the buds are opening—making April the perfect quiz subject for budding geniuses. Score yourself *genius* if you get all 10 of these questions . . . and if less than 5, crown yourself an April Fool.

1. What famous work begins "Whan that Aprill with his shoures soote"?
2. Who played the love interests in the 1952 film APRIL IN PARIS?
3. Who made both a movie and a hit record called "April Love"?
4. Who wrote "Oh, to be in England, now that April's there"?
5. Who said "April is the cruellest month"?
6. Name the 1969 romantic comedy starring Jack Lemmon, Catherine Deneuve, Peter Lawford, Harvey Korman, Sally Kellerman, Myrna Loy, and Charles Boyer.
7. Name the author of "O! how this spring of love resembleth the uncertain glory of an April day."
8. What is the birthstone for April?
9. How many days hath April?
10. Who introduced "April Showers" on the Broadway stage from a runway jutting into the audience?

APRIL FOOLS

(Answers)

1. Geoffrey Chaucer's THE CANTERBURY TALES
2. Ray Bolger and Doris Day
3. Pat Boone
4. Robert Browning
5. T.S. Eliot
6. THE APRIL FOOLS
7. William Shakespeare
8. Diamond
9. 30
10. Al Jolson

BONDED FOR LIFE

The James Bond habit is one not easily broken. In fact, if the Bond bug has bitten you, these ten questions won't even whet your appetite . Short of 007 himself, could anything . . . ?

1. What is the significance of a Double-0 (as in 007) classification?
2. Bond has pitted himself against both SMERSH and SPECTRE. What does each mean?
3. By what name is Paco ''Pistols'' Scaramanga better known?
4. Who's the man with the Midas touch?
5. Who was Tracy di Vicenzo?
6. What became of her?
7. Which adventure takes 007 to Crab Key Island, Honeychile Rider, and a bird guano front?
8. Who plays Bond in ON HER MAJESTY'S SECRET SERVICE?
9. What was Sean Connery's first James Bond film? His last?
10. The James Bond beset by ''Jaws'' in MOONRAKER and THE SPY WHO LOVED ME is played by ___________ ?

BONDED FOR LIFE

(Answers)

1. License to kill in the line of duty

2. SMERSH is a Russian counterspy organization. The name means "Death to Spies." SPECTRE means Special Executive for Counterintelligence, Terrorism, Revenge, and Extortion.

3. The Man with the Golden Gun

4. Auric Goldfinger

5. Tracy was the daughter of Draco (Bond ally and leader of France's powerful Union Corse) and also Bond's wife.

6. SPECTRE leader Blofeld killed her immediately after her wedding to Bond.

7. DOCTOR NO

8. George Lazenby

9. DOCTOR NO . . .
   NEVER SAY NEVER

10. Roger Moore

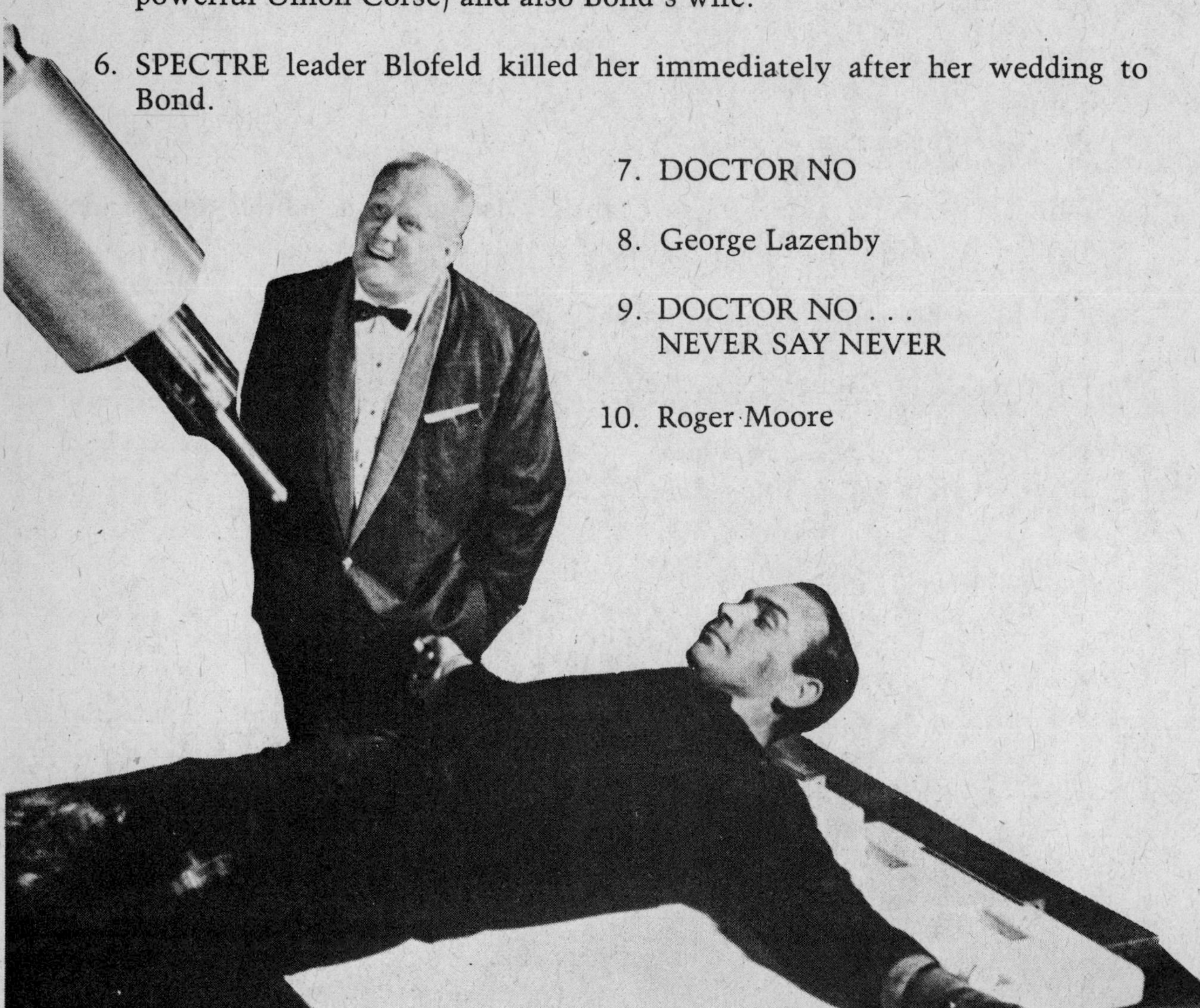

COIN OF THE REALM

Quick. Close your eyes and put your hand in your pocket. Do you know what you'll find there? How about if you were in Paris, or Madrid, or Moscow? Do you know what you'd find then.

If you answered "just the lining of my pocket" to the above questions, I can't tell you how grateful I am that you spent your last few cents to buy this book . . . .

1. On a new penny, where do you find the second "representation" of Lincoln?
2. What was the face value of the U.S. gold eagle?
3. What important U.S. institution began operations in 1792?
4. What Chilean coin is named after a South American bird?
5. Coins like the Czechoslovakian koruna and the Danish krone are named in honor of what concept?
6. How do we get the word "dollar" from St. Joachim's name?
7. What Peruvian coin has a Spanish name meaning "the sun"?
8. Before they also came to refer to coins, words like pound, peso, and lira referred to what?
9. The colon of El Salvador and Costa Rica is named after ___________?
10. A Panamian coin is named after Vasco Nunez de ___________?

COIN OF THE REALM

(Answers)

1. The little dot inside the Lincoln Monument is Lincoln's statue.
2. $10
3. The U.S. Mint
4. Condor
5. They are named for the *crown*, or royal authority.
6. Some four centuries ago, a coin was minted in St. Joachimsthal, Bohemia. It became known as a Joachimsthaler, then a thaler, and when the idea entered the English language, a dollar.
7. Sol
8. Weight
9. Christopher Columbus (in Spanish, Cristobal Colon)
10. Balboa

EATI GOURM T

Ever since the first man and woman set out on the sea of life—creating the original "Adam and Eve on a raft"—foods have gone by people's names for all kinds of reasons.

If this doesn't bother you, consider the poor Earl of Shrewsbury, whose name was replaced on his tasty creation by the man who did him in—the Earl of Sandwich.

Now, what would you call a sumptuous deli named after Mrs. Steve Lawrence?

1. What sauce is named for the port in which the Duke of Richelieu discovered it?

2. A toast and a peach dish are both named after Australian opera star __________ ?

3. Oysters broiled or baked with spinach and herbs on a bed of rock salt are called __________ ?

4. What crackers are named for the Presbyterian minister who promoted them as a way to combat alcoholism?

5. What coffee concoction is named after the Capuchin monks?

6. What liqueur stamped "D.O.M." was first made by monks?

7. Where do we get the word "booze"?

8. Both chicken and veal __________ are named for a battle Napoleon fought in 1800.

9. What beef-in-pastry combination is named after Napoleon's greatest adversary?

10. What sliced beef dish is named after a 19th-century Russian count?

EATIE GOURMET

(Answers)

1. Mayonnaise
2. Nellie Melba
3. Oysters Rockefeller
4. Graham Crackers
5. Cappucino
6. Benedictine . . . *D.O.M.* stands for the Latin *Deo Optimo Maximo,* "To God the Best, the Greatest."
7. From E. Booze, an American who bottled whiskey under his own name in the 1800s.
8. Marengo
9. Beef Wellington
10. Beef Stroganoff

A FOOD FRIBBLE

Napoleon's chefs have made culinary history. So have his troops. It is said they burned the flags he kissed when he said farewell to his men—and then they ate the ashes!

TWO HEARTS THAT BEAT AS ONE

Match each swooning sweetheart with her dashing swain in this scintillating selection of great lovers from history and fiction . . .

1. Abelard	a. Lord Bothwell
2. Empress Catharine	b. Dulcinea
3. Lola Montez	c. Marie Walewska
4. Alice	d. Heloise
5. Mary Queen of Scots	e. Nell Gwyn
6. Napoleon	f. Prince Potemkin
7. Don Quixote	g. King Ludwig of Bavaria
8. King Charles II	h. Cressida
9. Troilus	i. Mr. Montague
10. Ms. Capulet	j. Ralph

Answers: 1*d*, 2*f*, 3*g*, 4*j*, 5*a*, 6*c*, 7*b*, 8*e*, 9*h*, 10*i*

AROUND THE WORLD IN 80 FLICKS— THIRD LEG

Do you feel like Lowell Thomas yet? David Niven? The Road Runner? It's way too early to drop out—not with five more of these AROUND THE WORLD IN FLICKS matching quizzes on your itinerary later in this book. So catch your breath—which is much easier than catching a plane—and get to work on the third leg of your journey . . . .

1. HATARI!	a. West Point
2. ROSALIE	b. Nebraska
3. PORK CHOP HILL	c. Berlin
4. THE BOBO	d. Korea
5. BOYS TOWN	e. Hawaii
6. DIAMOND HEAD	f. Tanganyika
7. THE LEOPARD	g. Barcelona
8. GRAND HOTEL	h. Ireland
9. MARA MARU	i. Sicily
10. THE QUIET MAN	j. Manila

Answers: 1 f, 2 a, 3 d, 4 g, 5 b, 6 e, 7 i, 8 c, 9 j, 10 h.

THE DEVIL YOU SAY

It's time for a little innocent mischief. And you really don't have to sell your soul to come up with a red hot perfect score!

1. Who, according to German legend, sells his soul to the Devil in exchange for youth and another shot at worldly pleasure?
2. What's the name of the Devil to whom #1 sells his soul?
3. In what short story does a New England farmer sell his soul to the Devil, then win it back in court—thanks to a great American orator?
4. What was the fallen angel's name before he became Satan?
5. What and where is the Devil's Triangle?
6. What goes into a Devil's Cocktail?
7. How do you "beat the Devil's tattoo"?
8. To what island off French Guiana were the most dangerous French convicts sent—including Papillon, who escaped?
9. What is the function of the Devil's Advocate?
10. In the movie THE STORY OF MANKIND, mankind is on trial and the Devil himself is the Devil's advocate. Who plays the Devil?

THE DEVIL YOU SAY

(Answers)

1. Faust

2. Mephistopheles

3. THE DEVIL AND DANIEL WEBSTER (by Stephen Vincent Benet)

4. Lucifer

5. It's located between Bermuda and the United States. Some 100 planes and ships have disappeared from the area without a trace. The Devil's Triangle is also called The Bermuda Triangle.

6. Port wine, dry vermouth, and lemon juice

7. Keep drumming your fingers or your feet or a pencil, making infernal rapping noises until everyone in the room is nervous and uncomfortable.

8. Devil's Island

9. Originally a term used only by the Church, it now means anyone who upholds the opposite opinion in an argument—more to make the argument two-sided than to present a real personal conviction.

10. Vincent Price

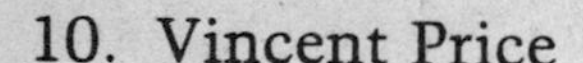

SWEET TOOTH

Okay, America, you consume some 4 billion pounds of sweets each year. Let's hope you know something about them besides the fact that they make your tummies happy . . . .

1. What major ingredient did Milton Hershey add to chocolate to provide the chocolate bars we know today?
2. According to Aztec legend, what happened to the god who brought chocolate to mankind?
3. What's another name for the hospital helper who wears a striped uniform?
4. In the poem "A Visit From St. Nicholas," what sort of visions dance in the childrens' heads?
5. Who's the little girl in PEANUTS who plays such a great game of baseball?
6. When it first came to Europe, the upper classes kept chocolate to themselves and drank it (without sugar) in enormous quantities. Why?
7. Name the Oscar Straus comic opera that became a Nelson Eddy-Rise Stevens movie.
8. What plant provides the basic ingredient of chocolate?
9. What Chubby Checkers dance became a nation-wide fad overnight?
10. In what TV Western did Will Hutchins star as Tom Brewster?

SWEET TOOTH

(Answers)

1. Milk (as in milk chocolate)

2. Because the rest of the gods didn't want to share it, they punished Quetzalcoatl by flaying him alive.

3. A candy striper

4. Sugar-plums

5. Peppermint Patty

6. It was said to be a stimulant and love potion—particularly since Montezuma, the Aztec chief, drank 50 cups a day to keep up with the 700 women in his harem.

7. THE CHOCOLATE SOLDIER

8. The cacao tree

9. The Peppermint Twist

10. SUGARFOOT

TOO PUNNY FOR WORDS

This is it. Your last chance to strut your synonym stuff. For these differently-spelled words that sound the same . . . can you supply the different meanings?

1. wave / waive
2. flair / flare
3. seer / sear
4. alter / altar
5. council / counsel
6. bleeding / bleating
7. diffuse / defuse
8. seine / sane
9. climb / clime
10. deign / Dane

Bonus Stumper: What's the difference between

abalone and *a bologna*?

TOO PUNNY FOR WORDS

(Answers)

1. *Wave* is to move to and fro or something that moves to and fro, like an ocean wave or a waving hand. *Waive* means to forego.

2. *Flair* is an instinctive sense of style or taste. *Flare* means to burn, or become excited, or to spread outward.

3. *Seer* is a prophet. *Sear* means to dry up or scorch.

4. *Alter* means to modify. *Altar* is the place where sacrifices are offered, or the front part in a church.

5. *Council* is an assembly formed to reach conclusions and to advise. *Counsel* means advice, or a piece of advice, or the person who gives the advice.

6. *Bleeding* is loss of blood. *Bleating* is the *baa-baa* sound made by sheep.

7. *Diffuse* means to spread or disperse in every direction. *Defuse* means to take the fuse away from something like a bomb or a temper tantrum.

8. *Seine* is a large net. *Sane* means rational.

9. *Climb* means to go up or go down. *Clime* is a poetic way of saying climate.

10. *Deign* means condescend. *Dane* is someone from Denmark.

Bonus Stumper: *Abalone* is a shelled sea creature that looks a little like a pin cushion when it dries. *A bologna* is a big, precooked seasoned sausage made of pork, beef and veal.

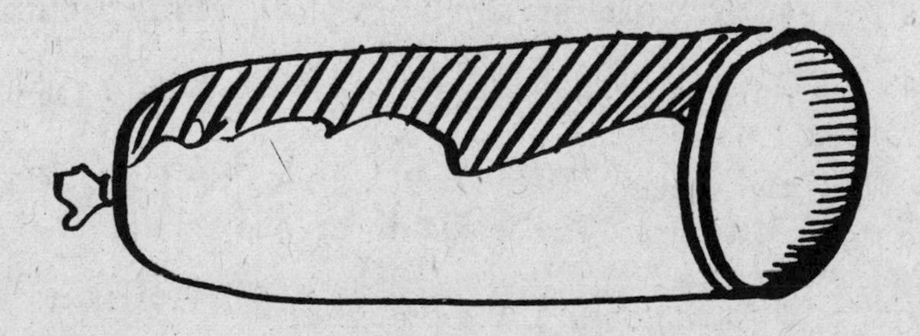

SUPERZOO

The world of superheroes would be super-dull without these awe-inspiring—did I hear you say awe-ful?—animals. Some have their own super powers. Some hang out with superheroes so they get superreputations. Some just dress funny.

Decide for yourself which is which . . . .

1. What's the name of The Phantom's gray wolf?

2. In SUPERMAN, who's the super-ape with super kryptonite vision, formerly known as Toto?

3. Who's Linda Lee's pet cat in SUPERGIRL?

4. In the Legion of Super-Pets, which is the super monkey?

5. Fearless Fosdick's arch enemy is a parrot named ___________ ?

6. Broom Hilda's pet buzzard is named ___________ ?

7. What's the name of Casper The Friendly Ghost's ghosthorse?

8. What's the name of the super-gorilla in FLASH comics?

9. Here-I-come-to-save-the-day means that which righteous superrodent is on the way?

10. The protoplasmic member of the Legion of Super-Pets that can assume any shape at all is named ___________ ?

SUPERZOO

(Answers)

1. Devil
2. Titano
3. Streaky
4. Beppo
5. Sydney
6. Gaylord
7. Nightmare
8. Grodd
9. Mighty Mouse
10. Proty II

PRETTY PICKLE

Even if you don't feel at home on the range, you shouldn't be in too much of a pickle with this quiz I've cooked up. If you are, stay out of the kitchen—or you're liable to find yourself in a real stew.

1. How many teaspoons in a tablespoon?
2. How many cups of butter in a pound?
3. What do you call it when you put something like almonds into boiling water, then into cold water?
4. What's it called when you expose the surface of meats, cheese dishes, etc., to direct heat?
5. What do you call the liquid something's been cooked in?
6. Heating just below the boiling point is called ___________ ?
7. What do you do to carrots or potatoes when you julienne them?
8. Who wrote the BOSTON COOKING SCHOOL COOK BOOK, published in 1896?
9. What language gives us the words saute, a la mode, and mayonnaise?
10. What isn't present in a fillet?

PRETTY PICKLE

(Answers)

1. 3
2. 2
3. Blanching
4. Broiling
5. Stock
6. Scalding
7. You cut them into very thin strips.
8. Fannie Farmer
9. French
10. The bone

FOR GOOD MEASURE

Man is a measuring animal. Measure this. Measure that. Somewhere in the course of his thirst for more things to measure, man invented trivia quizzes.

With this one, you can measure your knowledge of things that have to do with measurement.

1. Who wrote the play MEASURE FOR MEASURE?

2. According to the Greek scholar Protagoras, what is the measure of all things?

3. What is the numerical basis of the metric system?

4. Who complained when the metric system was introduced, "it will be a stumbling block and the source of difficulties for several generations . . . It's just tormenting the people with trivia!!!"?

5. Who wrote "The Love Song of J. Alfred Prufrock," and in it the lines "I have measured out my life with coffee spoons"?

6. What is the approximate weight of a U.S. bale of cotton?

7. What is meant by 18 karat gold?

8. How much wine in a magnum?

9. What is measured by a taximeter?

10. What measured 300 cubits by 50 cubits by 30 cubits?

FOR GOOD MEASURE

(Answers)

1. William Shakespeare

2. Man

3. The decimal system—all measures are multiples of 10.

4. Napoleon I

5. T.S. Eliot

6. Generally 500 pounds in the U.S., variable in other countries

7. A karat measures the purity of gold, indicating how many parts out of 24 are pure. 18 karat gold is 18/24 or 3/4 pure.

8. Two quarts

9. The fare due for a taxi ride

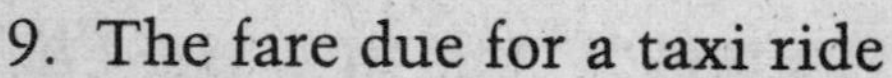

10. Noah's Ark

BATTER UP

Hey there, Fans! Don't strike out on these high hard ones. But if you do, just cry "Foul!"

1. Who is the only player ever to hit more home runs in a career than Babe Ruth? With how many home runs?

2. What team has played in more World Series games than any other, and how many times?

3. Who is the all-time leader in stolen bases in a career? With how many stolen bases?

4. Who has the highest batting average of all time, and what is it?

5. Who has the highest batting average for a single season? What average? What season?

6. Who was the last player to bat .400 in a single season, and in what year?

7. Who has the most career RBIs? How many?

8. What pitcher has the most strike outs for a season? How many?

9. What player has the longest consecutive hitting streak?

10. Who has the most grand slam home runs in a career?

BATTER UP

(Answers)

1. Hank Aaron with 755
2. New York Yankees . . . in 33 World Series, winning 22
3. Lou Brock, 938
4. Ty Cobb .367
5. Rogers Hornsby, .424 in 1924
6. Ted Williams in 1941
7. Hank Aaron has 2297
8. Nolan Ryan, 383 in 1973
9. Joe DiMaggio . . . 56 games in 1941
10. Lou Gehrig . . . 23

A METS FRIBBLE

Marvelous Marv Throneberry, dubbed the symbol of the luckless 1962 Mets, found fans in all the common folk who, like him, were drawn to life's stumbling blocks like dust to warm butter. Once, at a party thrown in his honor, he arrived so late that he couldn't find a seat among his admirers and had to eat across the street.

ROLL CALL

Sometimes two's company and three's a crowd. In show business, more than two is a group, a gang, a club, a brother act or a sister act. F'rinstance . . .

1. Name all five Marx Brothers. Who were they really?

2. Name the three Andrews Sisters.

3. Name the four Beatles.

4. Who were Al, Jim and Harry Joachim?

5. By what name are Cecile, Annette, Emilie, Marie and Yvonne better known?

6. Name Carol and Mike's three daughters and three sons on TV's THE BRADY BUNCH.

7. Name the Gibb Brothers, better known as the Bee Gees.

8. Name the Monkees.

9. Who were Annette, Darlene, Cubby, Karen, Doreen, Lonnie, Bobby, and a few dozen other kids who sang and danced across TV screens throughout the late 1950?

10. This is probably one of the all-time top ten Trivia questions: Name the Seven Dwarfs.

ROLL CALL

1. Chico (Leonard Marx), Harpo (Adolph Marx), Groucho (Julius Marx), Zeppo (Herbert Marx), and Gummo (Milton Marx)

2. Patty, Maxine and Laverne

3. John Lennon, George Harrison, Paul McCartney, and Ringo Starr (Richard Starkey)

4. Al, Jim and Harry Joachim were better known as The Ritz Brothers.

5. The Dionne Quintuplets

6. Marcia (Maureen McCormick), Jan (Eve Plumb, later Geri Reischl), Cindy (Susan Olsen), Greg (Barry Williams), Peter (Christopher Knight), Bobby (Mike Lookinland)

7. Barry, Robin, Maurice . . . Andy is a Gibb but not a Bee Gee.

8. Davy Jones, Peter Tork, Miky Dolenz, Mike Nesmith

9. The Mouseketeers on Walt Disney's MICKEY MOUSE CLUB

10. Bashful, Grumpy, Dopey, Doc, Sleepy, Sneezy, Happy

KARTOON KATS

Any cat lover will tell you the truth about cats. The truth is that cats would be happy to talk to people if they thought most people were half as smart as most cats.

Occasionally there are exceptions, particularly in cat-toon land, where cats don't care *who* they tell off!

Morris, you're not alone!

1. Name the cat who hangs around with Ignatz the mouse and Offissa Pup.

2. Sufferin' succotash, it's Tweetie Pie's feline foe.

3. In TOM AND JERRY, which one is the cat?

4. In MUTT AND JEFF, Mutt's son Cicero has a cat that's generally called "Cicero's Cat." But that's not her name. What is?

5. Name Smokey Stover's nutty cat with the bandaged tail.

6. What cat began his career with a bit part in a Peter Sellers movie, and soon became at least as popular as his bungling victim, Inspector Clouseau?

7. The name of this popular comic strip literally means "The Cat's Yowl Kids" because the kids act more like frisky cats than little humans. Name the strip.

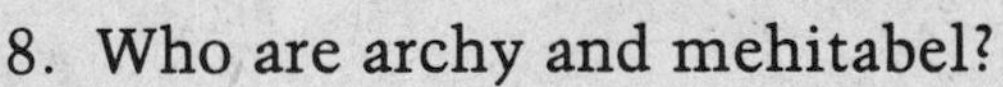

8. Who are archy and mehitabel?

9. Wacka-wacka! Who's the cat-toonist behind catwraps, catfolios, momcats, and all those cats that look like meatloaves?

10. What purring princess of pandemonium fell in love with Batman?

KARTOON KATS

1. Krazy Kat
2. Sylvester
3. Tom
4. Esmeralda
5. Spooky
6. The Pink Panther
7. The Katzenjammer Kids
8. Archy is a cockroach poet who jumps on typewriter keys to express himself (but he can't make capital letters) and mehitabel is a cat who claims her spirit once lived in the body of queen cleopatra.
9. B. Kliban
10. The Catwoman

FRIBBLE PHOBIA

Here are ten fribbilicious words to remind us all that the whole planet's one gigantic booby trap—and for each poor trapped booby, there's at least one phobic fear.

Ailourophobia:	Fear of Cats
Batophobia:	Fear of Walking
Clinophobia:	Fear of Going to Bed
Ergophobia:	Fear of Work
Harpaxophobia:	Fear of Robbers
Musophobia:	Fear of Mice
Nyctophobia:	Fear of Darkness
Pantophobia:	Fear of Everything
Pognophobia:	Fear of Beards
Teratophobia:	Fear of Monsters

TO SING'S THE THING

These movies, plays and books were already popular as non-musicals. But when a handful of tunesmiths came along and added songs and such, they became great all over again as musical smash hits. Can you—without hitting anyone or getting smashed—match the later versions with the shows that inspired them?

1. PYGMALION
2. ROMEO AND JULIET
3. MY SISTER EILEEN
4. THE MATCHMAKER
5. THE TAMING OF THE SHREW
6. I AM A CAMERA
7. 7½ CENTS
8. PRINCESS AND THE PEA
9. ANNA AND THE KING OF SIAM
10. THE TRAPP FAMILY SINGERS

a. WONDERFUL TOWN
b. KISS ME KATE
c. MY FAIR LADY
d. THE SOUND OF MUSIC
e. HELLO, DOLLY
f. WEST SIDE STORY
g. CABARET
h. THE PAJAMA GAME
i. ONCE UPON A MATTRESS
j. THE KING AND I

Answers:

1 c, 2 f, 3 a, 4 e, 5 b,
6 g, 7 h, 8 i, 9 j, 10 d

OUT OF *WHERE* BY SUNDOWN?

Suffrin' sixguns, it's true! Each of these vintage TV Westerns was tied to a town that had a name, if only so the bad guy could mean it when he said, "I've been thrown out of better towns than this before sundown."

Any sure as shootin' TV bad guy could score a perfect bullseye 10 on this matching quiz. Can you?

1. THE LIFE AND LEGEND OF WYATT EARP
2. ANNIE OAKLEY
3. HAVE GUN, WILL TRAVEL
4. THE VIRGINIAN
5. YANCY DERRINGER
6. BIG VALLEY
7. ZORRO
8. BONANZA
9. GUNSMOKE
10. THE LAWMAN

a. Monterey
b. Diablo
c. Stockton
d. Laramie
e. New Orleans
f. San Francisco
g. Medicine Bow
h. Virginia City
i. Dodge City
j. Dodge City and Tombstone

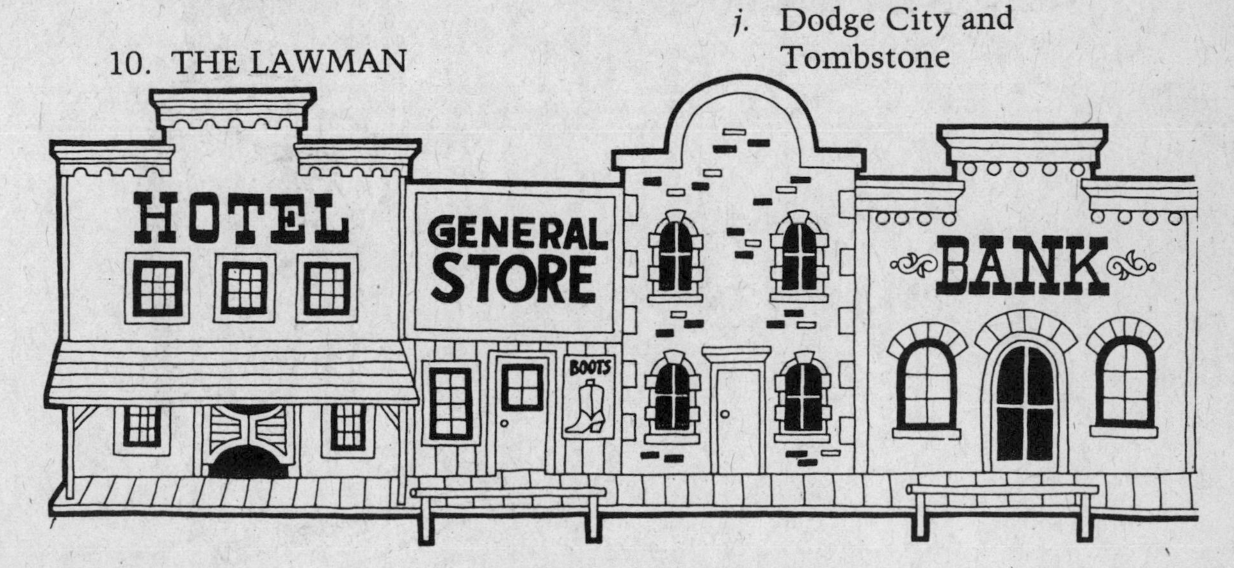

Answers: 1 *j*, 2 *b*, 3 *f*, 4 *g*, 5 *e*, 6 *c*, 7 *a*, 8 *h*, 9 *i*, 10 *d*

SEZ WHO TWO

You'll have absolutely no trouble at all with this star-studded endorsement matching quiz *if* you've been paying attention to the wise words that pour out of America's foremost faces. You know, the faces that grace your TV screen in these and other unforgettable commercials . . . .

1. Robert Morley	a. Kodak Ektralite
2. Michael Landon	b. Smith-Barney
3. Suzanne Somers	c. Polaroid One-Step
4. Luciano Pavarotti	d. Wesson
5. John Houseman	e. IBM Copiers
6. George Burns	f. British Airways
7. Mean Joe Greene	g. American Express
8. Florence Henderson	h. Diet 7-Up
9. James Garner	i. Livesavers
10. Lynda Carter and Don Rickels	j. Coke

Answers:

1*f*, 2*a*, 3*i*, 4*g*, 5*b*,
6*e*, 7*j*, 8*d*, 9*c*, 10*h*

SO PROUDLY WE HAIL

If you think "The Star Spangled Banner" is about the dawnserly light, it's time you took another look at our National Anthem. And another thing, the Pledge of Allegiance doesn't begin "I led the pigeons to the flag . . . ."

1. Who wrote the words of "The Star Spangled Banner"?
2. During what war?
3. What was the original title?
4. What does the first verse mean, anyway?
5. At what time of day does the anthem begin?
6. When last had he seen the flag?
7. What words reveal that the flag's still flying high?
8. What weapons are mentioned in the song?
9. In the third verse, how shall the flag wave?
10. In all three verses, over what shall it wave?

The Dawnserly Light

SO PROUDLY WE HAIL

(Answers)

1. Francis Scott Key

2. The War of 1812

3. "The Defense of Fort McHenry"

4. It means the flag had withstood the night-long battle against the forces of the British Royal Navy, and the American defenders of the fort, inspired by the flag, refused to surrender.

5. Dawn

6. At twilight's last gleaming

7. (The Stars and Stripes) were so gallantly streaming . . . o'er the ramparts.

8. Rockets and bombs

9. In triumph

10. O'er the land of the free and the home of the brave

SORRY, MR. SAURUS

Wouldn't you just love to bring prehistory alive? Probably not—unless you want it to gobble your face and trample you some. So why not settle for this lively quiz—and stop trying to dig up dinosaurs in your back yard.

1. *Dinosaur* comes from two Greek words, *deinos* and *sauros*—meaning what?
2. In what Troy Donahue movie does a prehistoric fish turn a prof into a caveman?
3. Movies aside, were dinosaurs ever as big as large houses?
4. Some dinosaurs walked on four legs, some on two. Generally speaking, how did their diets differ?
5. Who wrote the screenplay for THE BEAST FROM 20,000 FATHOMS?
6. Which gigantic dinosaur, whose name means *thunder lizard,* was so enormous it lived in swamps to help support its weight—but such a pussy cat that instead of fighting, it hid underwater when in danger?
7. Which dinosaur had a "three-horned face"?
8. Which meanie was the "king of dinosaurs"?
9. Who plays the human lovers in WHEN DINOSAURS RULED THE EARTH?
10. How did pterodactyl get around?

SORRY, MR. SAURUS

(Answers)

1. Terrible (*deinos*) lizard (*sauros*)
2. MONSTER ON THE CAMPUS
3. Absolutely—for instance, the brachiosaurus was the largest land animal of all time, half as long as a football field and about as tall as a stadium.
4. Generally speaking, the plant-eaters usually walked on four legs and the meat-eaters on two.
5. Ray Bradbury
6. The brontosaurus
7. The triceratops
8. The tyrannosaurus rex
9. Victoria Vetri and Robin Hawdon
10. By flying

THINK SHRINK

Some like Sigmund broiled, some like Sigmund Freud. You may even think Sigmund is half-baked, but if you complete this quiz correctly, you might give serious thought to buying a couch and starting your own practice....

1. The "inkblot" test is named after the man who invented it. Who?
2. What is it called when a dog's mouth waters not only over food but also when it hears a signal it has learned to associate with food?
3. Who was the psychologist who rejected Freud's theories in favor of a system of basic unconscious ideas or "archetypes"?
4. When you study the whole instead of individual elements, it's called ___________ from a German word meaning "pattern."
5. Who divides the mind into three parts—the id, the ego, and the superego?
6. What is it called when a son becomes so fond of his mother he's jealous of his father?
7. Whose theory is described in #6?
8. A morbid fear of narrow or enclosed places is called ___________ ?
9. Why isn't hydrophobia "a state of mind"?
10. Being overly suspicious with delusions of grandeur or persecution is called ___________ ?

THINK SHRINK

(Answers)

1. Rorschach
2. A Pavlovian ("conditioned") reflex
3. Carl Jung
4. Gestalt
5. Sigmund Freud
6. An Oedipus Complex
7. Sigmund Freud's
8. Claustrophobia
9. Although it can mean fear of water, it usually means rabies.
10. Paranoia

GRAVE QUESTIONS

In this case, getting there is more than half the fun. In fact, being there can be so bad that not everyone takes it lying down . . . .

1. What is taphophobia?

2. A tiny little spaceman in a cigar-shaped flying saucer plowed into a windmill and crashed to the ground in Aurora, Texas, in 1897. What became of his remains?

3. The silent film star so beloved that his funeral caused nation-wide suicides and a major riot in New York in 1926 was ___________ ?

4. When told the taciturn Calvin Coolidge had died, Dorothy Parker asked ___________ ?

5. What Robert Louis Stevenson - Lloyd Osbourne collaboration—later a Michael Caine - Peter Sellers movie—concerns the delivery of the wrong casket to the brothers Finsbury?

6. In the HAPPY DAYS episode where Fonzie fakes his own funeral after an explosion, what do people think is all that's left of him?

7. Advertised as the movie "with something to offend everyone," what Robert Morse - Jonathan Winters - Liberace vehicle is about the funeral business?

8. True or False—Bela Lugosi was buried in his Dracula costume?

9. What epitaph did W.C. Fields compose for himself?

10. Who wrote FUNERALS ARE FATAL?

GRAVE QUESTIONS

(Answers)

1. Fear of being buried alive
2. Local residents gave him and his craft a proper burial.
3. Rudolph Valentino
4. "How could they tell?"
5. THE WRONG BOX
6. A pile of ashes and his leather boots
7. THE LOVED ONE
8. True
9. "On the whole, I'd rather be in Philadelphia."
10. Agatha Christie

OFFICIAL FAST TALK

When it comes to fast talking, the government's got everyone beat—with acronyms, those words made from the first letters of a lot of words. For instance, there was talk awhile back in Washington about the ERISA (Employee Retirement Income Security Act). When Carter asked what it stood for, the Secretary of the Treasury told him, "Every Ridiculous Idea Since Adam."

Now, see what sense you can make of these other popular (not all government) acronyms. After all, why should Washington have a monopoly on fast talking?

1. RADAR
2. NASA
3. INTERPOL
4. CORE
5. VISTA
6. SONAR
7. EST
8. WAVES
9. USES
10. JOBS

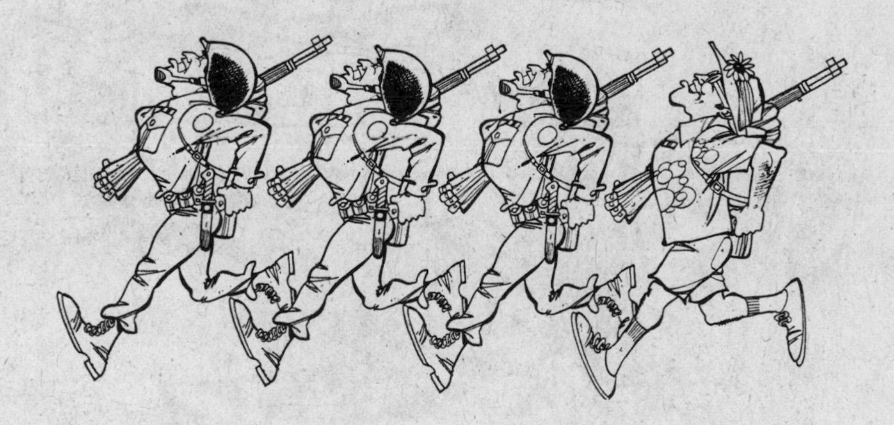

There has also been a CREEP, or Committee to Re-Elect the President, but that may be carrying acronymns too far.

OFFICIAL FAST TALK

(Answers)

1. Radio Detection and Ranging
2. National Aeronautics and Space Administration
3. International Criminal Police Organization
4. Congress of Racial Equality
5. Volunteers in Service to America
6. Sound Navigation and Ranging
7. Erhard Seminars Training
8. Women Accepted for Volunteer Emergency Service (Women's Reserve, USNR)
9. United States Employment Service
10. Job Opportunities in the Business Sector

THE MANE EVENT

You may not win the Triple Crown, even if you're an expert at the "Sport of Queens." But who cares, so long as you come into the home stretch miles ahead of the competition. You should, if you know your oats . . . .

1. Who originated the first sweepstakes horse race and to what did he lend his name?
2. Where is the Grand National Steeplechase held?
3. Where was the first U.S. thoroughbred racing held?
4. Name the three races that form the Triple Crown.
5. What is a steeplechase race?
6. What was so unusual about the winner of the 1980 Kentucky Derby?
7. Actor Jack Klugman's horse also ran in the 1980 Kentucky Derby. What's its name?
8. What were Man o' War's racing colors?
9. What famous jockey to England's Queen Mother is also a mystery writer and the author of ODDS AGAINST, BLOOD SPORT, and FLYING FINISH?
10. Eddie Arcaro rode five Kentucky Derby winners. How many can you name?

THE MANE EVENT

(Answers)

1. The 12th Earl of Derby originated the first horse racing sweepstakes in 1780, and they have been known as the Epsom or English *Derby* ever since.

2. It's been held annually at Aintree Course, Liverpool, England since 1839.

3. Saratoga Springs, New York, in 1863

4. Kentucky Derby, Preakness, Belmont

5. A steeplechase is a horse race with obstacles like water holes and hurdles to simulate rough natural conditions.

6. Genuine Risk was the first filly to win the Kentucky Derby since Regret in 1915.

7. Jaklin Klugman

8. Black and yellow

9. Dick Francis

10. Lawrin (1938), Whirlaway (1941), Hoop, Jr. (1945), Citation (1948), Hill Gail (1952)

KA-BOOM!

What happens when Hollywood sets its heart on a disaster movie? KA-BOOM, KA-BLOOEY, and these edge-of-your-chair flicks. If you're taking this quiz, KA-MON, hurry up—tomorrow may be too late . . . .

1. What's the 1970 airline disaster movie that won Helen Hayes an Oscar for her role as a stowaway?

2. Ingrid Bergman marries a fisherman then a famous mountain blows its top in ___________ ?

3. What Jeanette MacDonald-Clark Gable-Spencer Tracy movie is about a major West Coast earthquake?

4. What narrow escape makes The Unsinkable Molly Brown unsinkable?

5. What's the setting of A NIGHT TO REMEMBER?

6. What disaster provides the climax for IN OLD CHICAGO?

7. In which Elizabeth Taylor movie is a vast estate destroyed by an elephant stampede?

8. Which Sherlock Holmes film involves a train wreck, a major fire, and other off-stage disasters?

9. What 1976 spoof of disaster movies concerns the adventures of the Cyclops/Coyote, a nuclear-powered bus?

10. What luxury vehicle bursts into flames and fiery death in the movie THE HINDENBURG?

KA-*BOOM!*

(Answers)

1. AIRPORT
2. STROMBOLI
3. SAN FRANCISCO
4. She survives the sinking of the Titanic.
5. The sinking of the Titanic
6. The Chicago fire of 1871
7. ELEPHANT WALK
8. SHERLOCK HOLMES AND THE VOICE OF TERROR
9. THE BIG BUS
10. Germany's hydrogen-filled zeppelin *Hindenburg*

IN THEIR OWN WRITE

When the great and famous tell on themselves in their own autobiographies, it's usually kiss-and-tell-all and then some. Some what?

Some what-not, naturally, what else . . .?

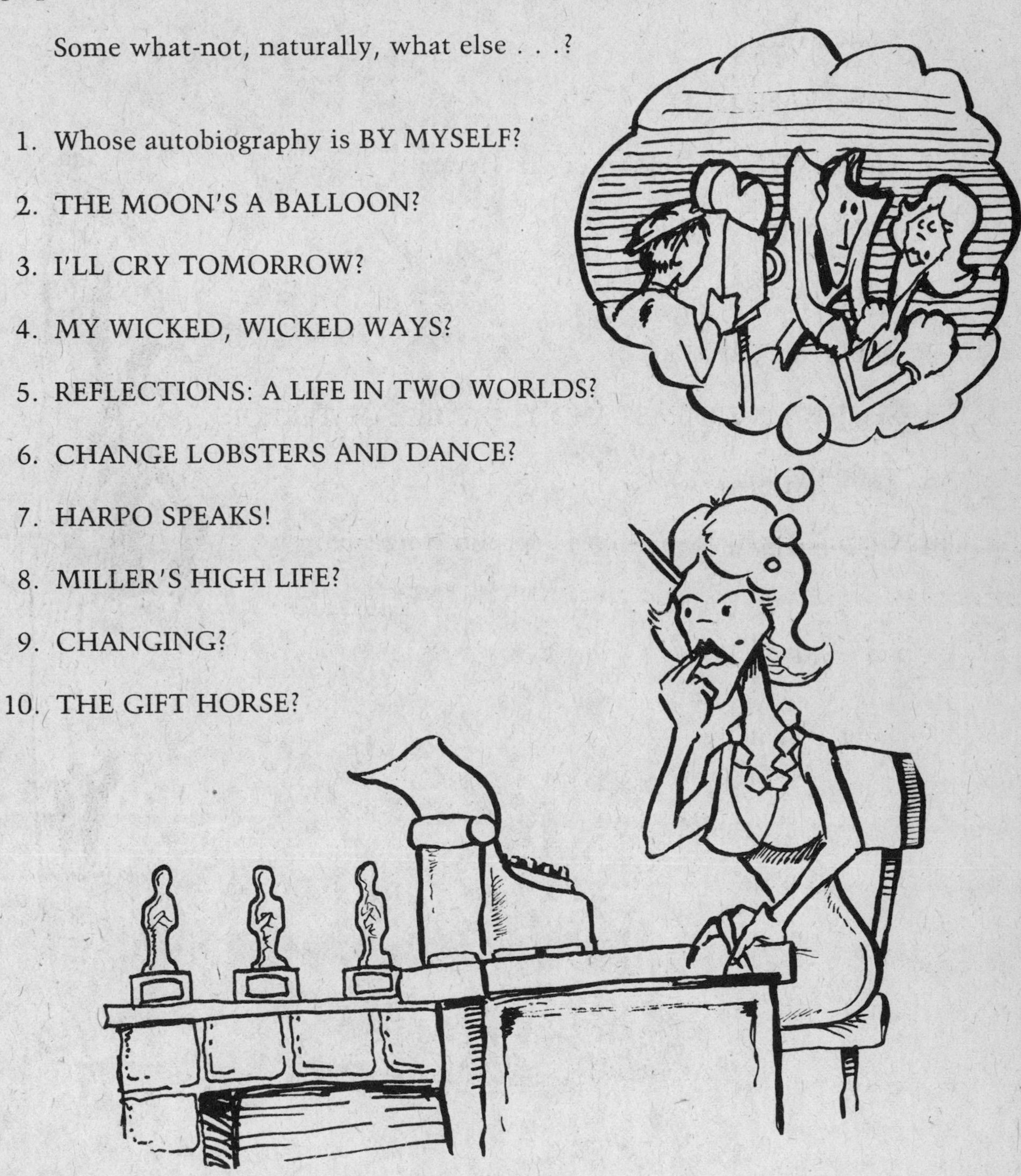

1. Whose autobiography is BY MYSELF?
2. THE MOON'S A BALLOON?
3. I'LL CRY TOMORROW?
4. MY WICKED, WICKED WAYS?
5. REFLECTIONS: A LIFE IN TWO WORLDS?
6. CHANGE LOBSTERS AND DANCE?
7. HARPO SPEAKS!
8. MILLER'S HIGH LIFE?
9. CHANGING?
10. THE GIFT HORSE?

Bonus Stumper: Who is MOMMY DEAREST about and who wrote it?

IN THEIR OWN WRITE

(Answers)

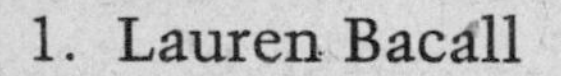

1. Lauren Bacall
2. David Niven
3. Lillian Roth
4. Errol Flynn
5. Ricardo Montalban
6. Lilli Palmer
7. Harpo Marx
8. Ann Miller
9. Liv Ullmann
10. Hildegarde Neff

Bonus: Joan Crawford by Christina Crawford, her adopted daughter

HUES-FUL TUNES

You don't have to be Judy Garland to sing up a rainbow of songs. But can you warble—or even fill in the missing parts of the names of—these colorful favorites? Some are as old as them thar hills, while others are as new as Bobby Vinton and the Beatles.

1. "__________ Shoes with __________ Shoelaces"
2. "Cherry __________ and Apple Blossom __________"
3. "Mood __________"
4. "Deep __________"
5. "Ever__________"
6. "__________ Velvet"
7. "Jeanie with the Light __________ Hair"
8. "__________ Submarine"
9. "__________berry Hill"
10. "Look for the __________ Lining"

HUES-FUL TUNES

(Answers)

1. Tan . . . pink
2. Pink . . . white
3. Indigo
4. Purple
5. green

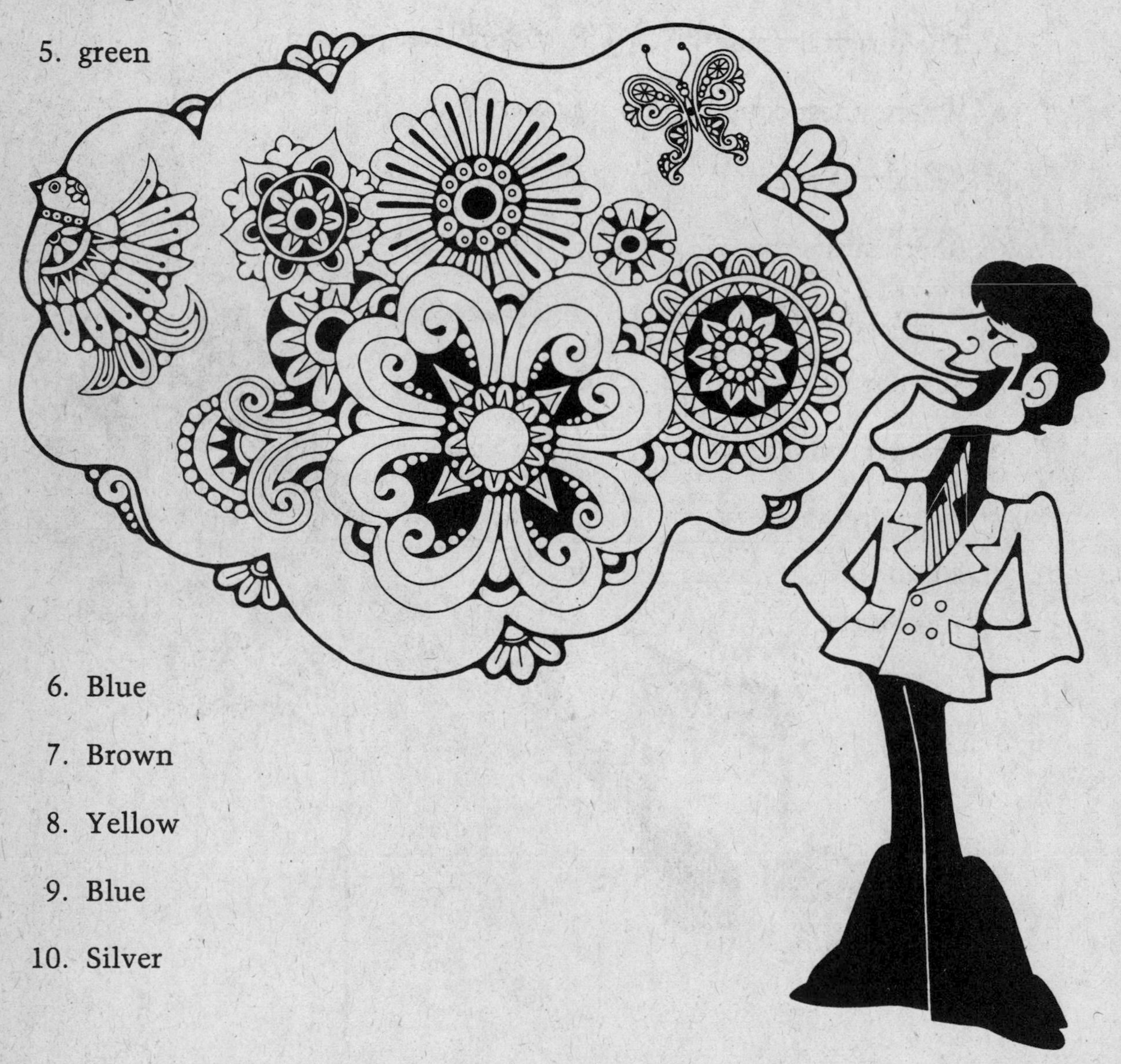

6. Blue
7. Brown
8. Yellow
9. Blue
10. Silver

GWTW

A box-office goldmine that's earned over $75,000,000 to date, GONE WITH THE WIND is a trivia goldmine too—so start digging and maybe you'll strike it rich with a perfect score on this matching quiz.

1. Scarlett's home
2. Ashley's home
3. The hospital scene
4. Where Rhett comes from
5. Scarlett O'Hara
6. Rhett Butler
7. Brent Tarleton
8. Scarlett's sister
9. Scarlett's rival
10. Ashley Wilkes

a. Melanie Hamilton
b. Leslie Howard
c. George Reeves
d. Vivien Leigh
e. Twelve Oaks
f. Clark Gable
g. Charleston
h. Suellen
i. Atlanta
j. Tara

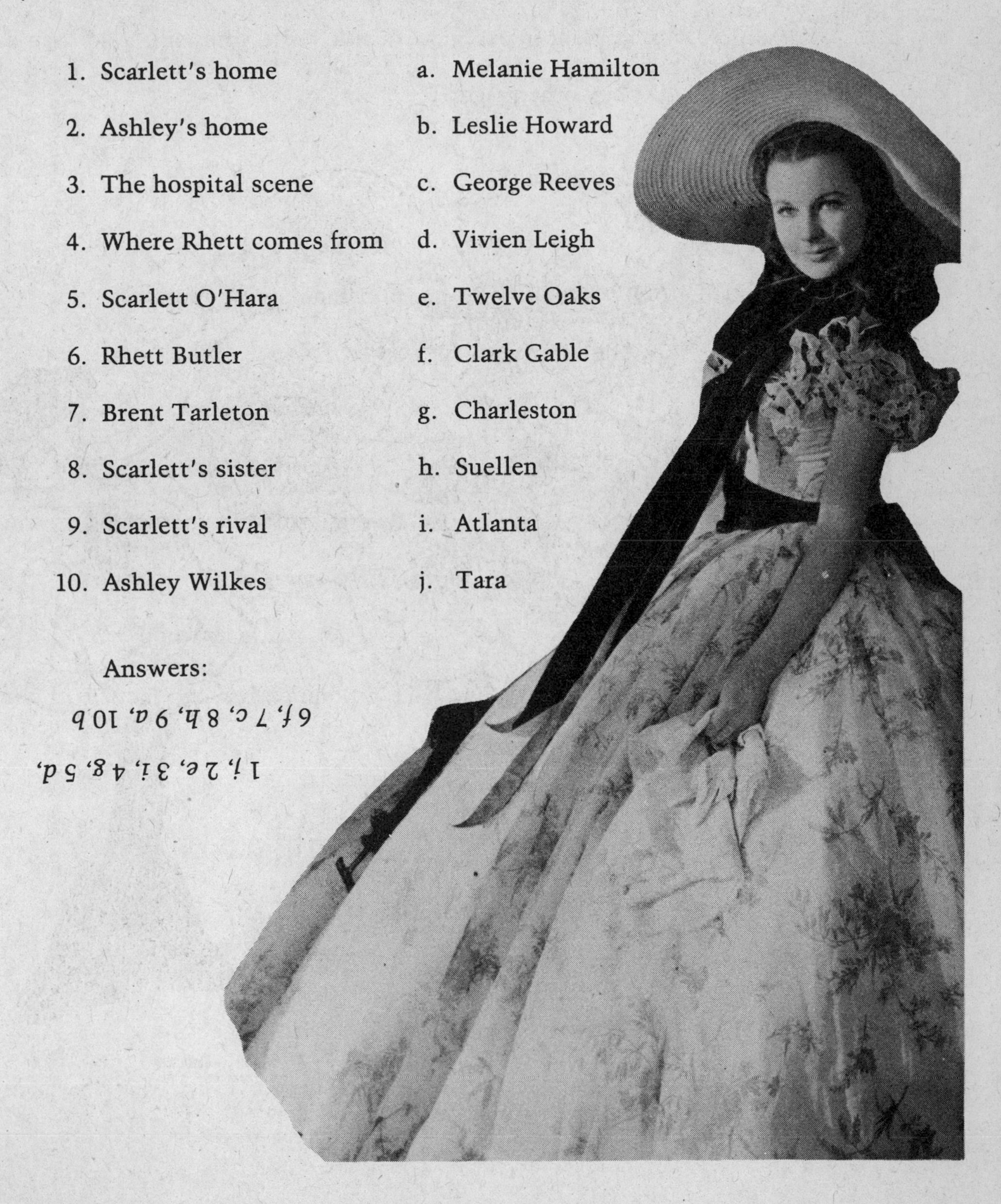

Answers:

1*j*, 2*e*, 3*i*, 4*g*, 5*d*,
6*f*, 7*c*, 8*h*, 9*a*, 10*b*

ANYTOWN, U.S.A.

To make sure there's no doubt in your mind that TV's sitcom families are *just like yours*, they're given whole addresses, most of which you'll never find on a map because either the streets or towns don't exist, or no one ever tells you what *state* they're in.

But unless you're planning to pay them a visit, who cares—so long as you can match each show with the correct address. After all, one *state* of *confusion* is just like any other, right?

1. LEAVE IT TO BEAVER
2. I LOVE LUCY
3. THE DICK VAN DYKE SHOW
4. FATHER KNOWS BEST
5. MAUDE
6. THE HONEYMOONERS
7. MARY HARTMAN, MARY HARTMAN
8. THE PARTRIDGE FAMILY
9. ALL IN THE FAMILY
10. THE FLINTSTONES

a. 345 Stone Cave, Bedrock
b. 623 E. 68 Street, New York
c. 211 Pine Street, Mayfield
d. 607 S. Maple, Springfield
e. 39 Crenshaw, Tuckahoe
f. 704 Houser, Queens
g. 698 Sycamore, San Pueblo
h. 328 Chauncey, Brooklyn
i. 343 Bratner, Fernwood
j. 148 Bonnie Meadow, New Rochelle

Answers: 1 *c*, 2 *b*, 3 *j*, 4 *d*, 5 *e*, 6 *h*, 7 *i*, 8 *g*, 9 *f*, 10 *a*—although some of these street numbers (rarely the street names) have changed over the years because things like this don't matter to TV writers the way they matter to you and me.

TILE TRIVIA

It's something like a crossword puzzle, even a little like dominoes. It's played with lettered tiles—and your set should have a hundred of them unless your cat has knocked a few under the sofa.

It's Scrabble, of course . . . although when you've played it enough, you may know it as $S_1C_3R_1A_1B_3B_3L_1E_1$ . . . .

1. How many tiles are in a "hand"?

2. How many blank tiles are there in a game?

3. What is the point value of a blank tile?

4. What are the two highest-ranking letters in Scrabble?

5. Which of these letters is worth more than one point—N, O, T, X, U?

6. What color is a "double letter score" square?

7. What color is a "triple letter score" square?

8. How many squares are on a playing board?

9. What color is the central square, and what is its significance?

10. What bonus do you get if you use all 50 of your tiles in one turn?

TILE TRIVIA

(Answers)

1. Seven

2. Two

3. Under official rules, it has no point value, although players sometimes agree in advance to give it the value of the letter it represents.

4. Q and Z, worth 10 points each

5. X, worth 8 points

6. Pale blue

7. Red

8. 225 . . . the board is 15 squares by 15 squares

9. It is pink. The first player must cover it with the first word of the game. Because it is pink it is a "double word score" square, automatically doubling the point value of the first word of the game.

10. An additional 50 points

MORE MONSTERS

Subject to the right curse, the wrong mutation, or enough radiation, any she, it, them, or thing can become a monster. Or so Hollywood tells us in these mind-gouging flicks.

1. In SHE, is "she" a monster?
2. In the horror film IT, what's "it" do?
3. Describe THEM.
4. What sort of monsters roam in NIGHT OF THE LEPUS?
5. What city does Gorgo threaten?
6. What about Reptilicus?
7. Who played the teen-age werewolf in I WAS A TEEN-AGE WEREWOLF?
8. Who played the thing in THE THING?
9. Though sentenced to the electric chair in MAN-MADE MONSTER, the M.M.M. doesn't die there. Why?
10. What is THE GORILLA MAN about?

MORE MONSTERS

(answers)

1. Both SHE and "she" are monsters of longevity. There have been seven silent and several sound versions—with the 1934 entry starring Helen Gahagan and the 1965 edition starring Ursula Andress. "She," by the way, is eternally beautiful though 2000 years old, and waits for her lover with a vengeance in darkest Africa. But when he comes, she ages all 20 centuries and burns to a crisp before our eyes.

2. A statue comes to life, and it becomes a murderer.

3. Them's giant mutant ants and them's swarming all over Los Angeles.

4. 150-lb. rabbits

5. London

6. Stockholm

7. Michael Landon

8. James Arness

9. He's immune to electricity.

10. Gotcha! It's about a plot by pro-Nazis to frame an RAF pilot. The part about a gorilla is a symbol (or an outright lie, depending on how you feel about symbolism.)

CANINE COMICS

You'll be in the doghouse with puppy-fanciers the world over if you can't identify these funny-page Fidos . . .

1. "The hound that's almost human." Created by Alex Graham, his thought balloons tell all.

3. Woodstock's beagle buddy.

3. Dondi's dog.

4. Blondie and Dagwood Bumstead's pooch.

5. Mark Trail's St. Bernard.

6. Dennis Mitchell's partner in crime.

7. Little Annie Rooney's rag-tag companion.

8. Little Orphan Annie's woolly mutt.

9. Superman's super-hound.

10. Sergeant Orville Snorkel's perky pup.

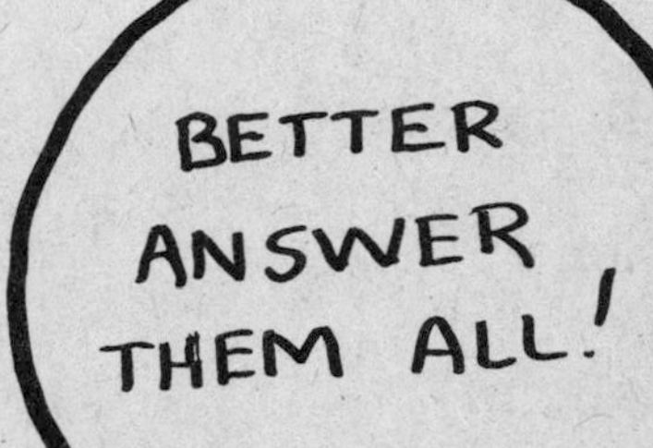

CANINE COMICS

(answers)

1. Fred Basset
2. Snoopy
3. Queenie
4. Daisy
5. Andy
6. Ruff
7. Zero
8. Sandy
9. Krypto
10. Otto

QUIZ IN RED AND BLUE

Roses are red, violets are blue, the subject of this quiz is things that are too. Now sharpen your wits. (So what else is new?)

1. What do they call the laws that regulate public behavior, particularly the use of alcoholic beverages, on Sundays?
2. Baron von Richthofen's nickname.
3. Newspaper of the Soviet Defense Ministry.
4. The Gainsborough masterpiece painted to disprove the theory that masses of the color blue ruin artistic compositions.
5. The 1930 German movie that launched the career of Marlene Dietrich.
6. Nickname for the state of Kentucky.
7. The Gable-Harlow film which was remade some 20 years later as the Gable-Gardner film MOGAMBO.
8. What do they call it when the skies take on strange colors after volcanic eruptions or major forest fires?
9. It measures 169,000 square miles and about 1600 feet deep.
10. The short-running TV series about an amnesia victim whose identity had some mysterious connection with two remembered words. (Do you know what the words meant when they were finally remembered?)

QUIZ IN RED AND BLUE

(answers)

1. Blue laws
2. The Red Baron
3. "Red Star"
4. "The Blue Boy"
5. THE BLUE ANGEL
6. "The Bluegrass State"
7. RED DUST
8. "Blue Moon"
9. The Red Sea
10. CORONET BLUE . . . and the show folded so quickly that the wrap-up episode was never filmed, leaving viewers forever in the dark about the meaning of the words and the poor guy's identity.

BEASTS FROM THE EAST

If it weighs two tons, has junk sticking out all over it, and flies, it's either a garbage truck or one of those weird monsters from a Japanese movie and . . . it's . . . creeping . . . through . . . your . . . window . . . RIGHT . . . *NOW!*

Can you give its correct name?

Under the circumstances, does it matter?

1. Describe Gamera.
2. SERPICO, GIDGET, VARAN, DOGORA—which is the monster jellyfish?
3. What kind of monster is Atragon?
4. To what city does Rodan lay waste?
5. What's Raymond Burr's role in GODZILLA, KING OF THE MONSTERS?
6. In GHIDRAH, THE THREE-HEADED MONSTER, who finally defeats it?
7. In KING KONG VERSUS GODZILLA, who wins?
8. What do they call Godzilla in Japan?
9. Godzilla as hero defeats a creature generated by industrial waste and factory pollution on GODZILLA VS. __________ ?
10. It's who vs. who in GODZILLA ON MONSTER ISLAND?

BEASTS FROM THE EAST

(answers)

1. Gamera is a jet-propelled prehistoric turtle of incredible proportions who hurls through the skies like a frisbee.

2. Dogora is the jellyfish . . . Serpico's a cop, Gidget's a girl midget, and Varan is a monster bat from the movie of the same name.

3. A giant submarine

4. Tokyo

5. Steve Martin, investigative reporter

6. Mothra, Rodan, and Godzilla—one per head

7. In the Japanese version Godzilla wins. In the U.S. version, Kong does.

8. Gojira

9. THE SMOG MONSTER

10. Godzilla and Anguirus against Ghidra and Gigan

STAR WARS STRIKES BACK

First came STAR WARS. It made more money than any movie in history. But they didn't stop there. Would *you*—if you'd just made a cool $400 million?

Then came THE EMPIRE STRIKES BACK, with a rubbery grey-green goodguy about 20 times as old as Captain Kirk and half the height of Superman, and the world can only say more, *more, MORE!*

Well, here's more, in the form of a STAR WARS quiz.

World, you never had it so good.

1. Who's the droid who looks a little like a metal cookie jar?

2. Who's the black-helmeted evil demon of The Empire?

3. What role did Mark Hamill create?

4. What's Sir Alec Guinness's role?

5. What is the name of Luke's troll-like advisor in THE EMPIRE STRIKES BACK?

6. Who plays Princess Leia?

7. Who's the huge Wookie co-pilot of Millennium Falcon?

8. For what contribution to STAR WARS did John Barry win an Academy Award?

9. The sandpeople of Tatooine ride woolly creatures called ___________ ?

10. Name R2-D2's shiny sidekick.

STAR WARS STRIKES BACK

(Answers)

1. R2-D2 (Artoo Detoo)
2. Darth Vader
3. Luke Skywalker
4. Obi-wan Kenobi
5. Yoda
6. Carrie Fisher
7. Chewbacca
8. He was film-production designer.
9. Banthas
10. 3-CPO (See Threepio)

NAME THAT TOWN

Cities have local crime, local politicians, and local taxes. They also have nicknames, usually bestowed by local residents who have an edge over everyone else when it comes to taking matching quizzes like this one. (If you know where each city gets its nickname, score yourself a few extra pats on the back.)

1. Abilene, Tx.	*a.* Lexington of Texas
2. Anniston, Ala.	*b.* Birthplace of Baseball
3. Cooperstown, N.Y.	*c.* City of Five Flags
4. Des Moines, Iowa	*d.* Brooklyn of the South
5. Detroit, Mich.	*e.* Hartford of the West
6. Gonzales, Tx.	*f.* Motown
7. Hartford, Ct.	*g.* City of Brotherly Love
8. Milwaukee, Wisc.	*h.* Athens of the West
9. Mobile, Ala.	*i.* Insurance City
10. Philadelphia, Pa.	*j.* Cream City

NAME THAT TOWN

1. *h* . . . because it is a center of culture, learning, and agriculture.

2. *d* . . . for its vast number of churches (!)

3. *b* . . . because it was once thought to be the site of the first baseball diamond in the U.S.

4. *e* . . . it is an insurance center like Hartford, Ct.

5. *f* . . . or *Motortown* because it is the center of the U.S. automobile industry.

6. *a* . . . just as Lexington and Concord is famous for the first shot of the American Revolution, Gonzales is famous for the first shot of the Texas Revolution.

7. *i* . . . it is the home of some of the largest insurance companies in America.

8. *j* . . . from the cream-white color of the bricks made of native clay.

9. *c* . . . because it has, at different times, belonged to Spain, France, Great Britain, the Confederate States of America, and the U.S.A.

10. *g* . . . a literal translation of its Greek name is *brotherly love*.

RUB-A-DUB-DUB

Ten stars in a tub. See if you can match them with the films that include their famous bathtub or shower scenes. At least get your feet wet with the first few—then if you find yourself in over your head, you can always holler for help from Rubber Duckie.

1. Gloria Swanson	a. RED DUST
2. Jean Harlow	b. ARABESQUE
3. Edward G. Robinson	c. MALE AND FEMALE
4. James Mason	d. LAURA
5. Sophia Loren	e. KEY LARGO
6. Trevor Howard	f. PSYCHO
7. Janet Leigh	g. LOLITA
8. Paulette Goddard	h. CLEOPATRA
9. Clifton Webb	i. SONS AND LOVERS
10. Richard Burton	j. UNCONQUERED

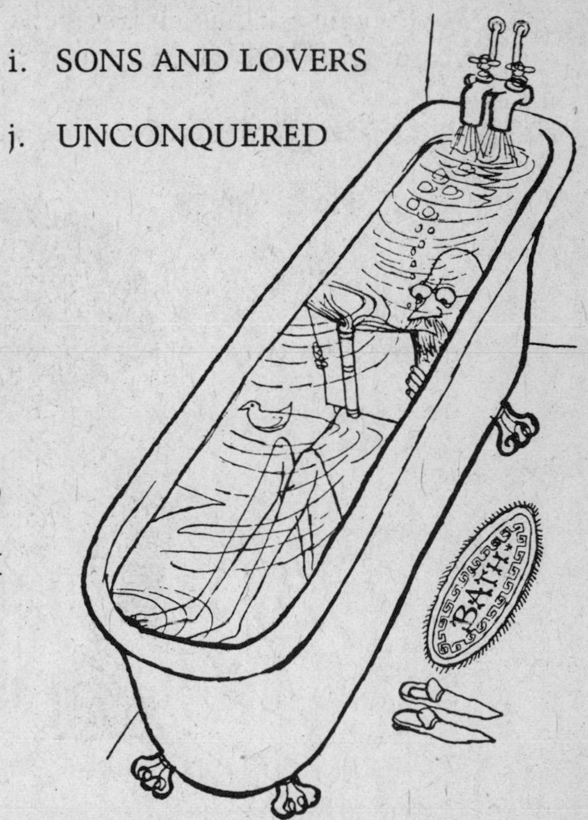

Answers:

1 c, 2 a, 3 e, 4 g, 5 b,
6 i, 7 f, 8 j, 9 d, 10 h

AROUND THE WORLD IN 80 FLICKS FOURTH LEG

I hope you're taking time to remember these movies as you match them with their locales—the great panoramas, the scenery, the atmosphere that makes you feel like you're there even if you're only sitting at home. Once you get in the proper mood, you may get so wrapped up in *these* memories that you'll forget to go on to legs 5, 6, 7, and 8, still ahead . . . .

1. THE FIRST TRAVELING SALESLADY	a. Amazon
2. THREE COINS IN THE FOUNTAIN	b. Paris
3. PIRANHA, PIRANHA	c. Canada
4. LOVE HAS MANY FACES	d. Rome
5. FUNNY FACE	e. Texas
6. SUMMERTIME	f. Kenya
7. ROSE MARIE	g. Venice
8. TOM JONES	h. Acapulco
9. BORN FREE	i. Miami
10. CLAMBAKE	j. England

Answers:

1 *e*, 2 *d*, 3 *a*, 4 *h*, 5 *b*,
6 *g*, 7 *c*, 8 *j*, 9 *f*, 10 *i*.

BAD BREAKS

On a bad break scale ranging from one to ten, a one would probably be something like breaking eggshells into your omelet and a ten would be what happened to Humpty Dumpty. Can you think of something worse than a ten? Don't even try. Just answer these questions about other people's bad breaks, and take your mind off your own . . . .

1. What bad break befalls the kidnappers in the story THE RANSOM OF RED CHIEF, by O. Henry?

2. Humpty Dumpty appears in what Lewis Carroll novel?

3. In #2, what does Humpty Dumpty say words mean?

4. What Woodward and Bernstein book of the late 1970s takes its name from the Humpty Dumpty rhyme?

5. What is #4 about?

6. Who plays Humpty Dumpty in the 1933 movie ALICE IN WONDERLAND?

7. In #6, who plays the Mock Turtle?

8. What is the name of the 1979 movie about townies and college students and the Little 500 bicycle race?

9. Name the Dana Andrews movie about the scientist who tries to harness the earth's energy but blows an enormous hunk out of its surface—himself included—instead.

10. In the TV series BROKEN ARROW, who played Cochise?

BAD BREAKS

(Answers)

1. They kidnap a kid so bratty that his father not only refuses to pay ransom but eventually makes *them* pay *him* to take the boy back.

2. THROUGH THE LOOKING-GLASS

3. Whatever he chooses them to mean

4. ALL THE PRESIDENT'S MEN

5. Nixon and the Watergate coverup

6. W.C. Fields

7. Cary Grant

8. BREAKING AWAY

9. CRACK IN THE WORLD

10. Michael Ansara

TENNIS, ANYONE?

The game of tennis is some 800 years old. But 800 years ago it was a matter of batting a cloth bag of hair over a rope. And players used hands, not racquets, something like volley ball. This goes to show that the Billie Jean Kings and Bobby Riggs of 12th Century France would have done very badly at this quiz compared to you . . . .

1. What vital item in a tennis game measures about 2½" across?
2. What is the length of a regulation tennis court?
3. What is the width for singles? For doubles?
4. What area falls between the baseline and the service line?
5. What word, coming from the French *l'oeuf* (egg) means zero in tennis?
6. The first point won by a player in a game is 15. The second is 30. What are the third and fourth?
7. If there is no 5-5 tie, which player wins the set?
8. If you miss on both your first and second serve, what is it called and how are you penalized?
9. What is a stroke called when it returns a ball before the ball has touched the ground?
10. What is it called when two players hit the ball back and forth?

TENNIS, ANYONE?

(Answers)

1. The tennis ball
2. 78 feet long
3. 27 feet . . . 36 feet
4. The backcourt
5. Love
6. 40 and "game"
7. The first player who wins six games
8. It's a "double fault" and you lose the point.
9. The volley
10. A rally

A FRIBBLE

Bill Tilden is the only man ever to win the U.S. Singles Championship at Forest Hills seven times. Six were consecutive!

AROUND THE WORLD IN 80 FLICKS— FIFTH LEG

By now you've reached the half-way mark with these AROUND THE WORLD IN FLICKS matching quizzes. Not bad at all, considering you don't need a passport and you don't need a single innoculation or shot. Best of all, unlike some of the folks in the movies below, you're not going to be shot *at*, so you can enjoy your trip without a care in the world!

1. CHARADE	a. South Pacific
2. DONOVAN'S REEF	b. Rio de Janeiro
3. FOUL PLAY	c. Norway
4. NOTORIOUS	d. San Francisco
5. GAMBIT	e. New York
6. THE QUILLER MEMORANDUM	f. Constantinople
7. DRUMS ALONG THE MOHAWK	g. Hong Kong
8. EDGE OF DARKNESS	h. Riviera
9. TO CATCH A THIEF	i. Berlin
10. TOPKAPI	j. Paris

Answers:

1*j*, 2*a*, 3*d*, 4*b*, 5*g*,
6*i*, 7*e*, 8*c*, 9*h*, 10*f*

RONALD REAGAN

LIGHTS, ACTION, REAGAN

Everyone knows Ronald Reagan, the President, actor, statesman, and matinee idol who said, "I have wondered at times what the Ten Commandments would have looked like had Moses run them through a state legislature."

If you knew that about Reagan, you may know everything else. In that case, you'll have no trouble with these questions.

1. For what work was he known before he became an actor?

2. What was his first film?

3. Of what professional actors' organizations was he president?

4. To what public post was he elected in 1966?

5. What's the title of his 1965 campaign autobiography?

6. In KNUTE ROCKNE, ALL AMERICAN, Pat O'Brien played the title role. What role did Reagan play?

7. For what role in the film CASABLANCA was he originally signed?

8. In the movie SANTA FE TRAIL, which had nothing to do with the Santa Fe Trail, what famous West Point graduate did he play?

9. Of what long-running TV dramatic show was he first the star and later the host and occasional star?

10. What was his last film?

LIGHTS, ACTION, REAGAN

(Answers)

1. He was a sports reporter.

2. LOVE IS ON THE AIR (1937)

3. Screen Actors Guild (president for 6 years) and the Picture Industry Council (president for 2 years).

4. Governor of the State of California

5. WHERE'S THE REST OF ME?

6. Reagan played the felled football hero "The Gipper."

7. He was originally signed for the part of Rick, who was eventually played by Humphrey Bogart.

8. George Armstrong Custer

9. General Electric Theater

10. LET THE WORLD GO FORTH (1965)

WHICH SIDE SHOULD I KICK?

Here are ten sets of adventurers and their sidekicks, and all you have to do is match them up. If they actually do go around kicking each other in the side, I guess someone has to *patch* them up too. But that's not your problem, unless your best friend wears a mask and calls you kemosabe.

1. Matt Dillon	a. Sancho
2. Don Quixote	b. Pancho
3. Cisco Kid	c. Lofty Craig
4. Napoleon Solo	d. Artemus Gordon
5. Andy Taylor	e. Illya Kuryakin
6. Jace Pearson	f. Ken Hutchinson
7. Annie Oakley	g. Barney Fife
8. James T. West	h. Chester Goode
9. Green Hornet	i. Clay Morgan
10. Dave Starsky	j. Kato

Answers:

1 h, 2 a, 3 b, 4 e, 5 g, 6 i, 7 c, 8 d, 9 j, 10 f

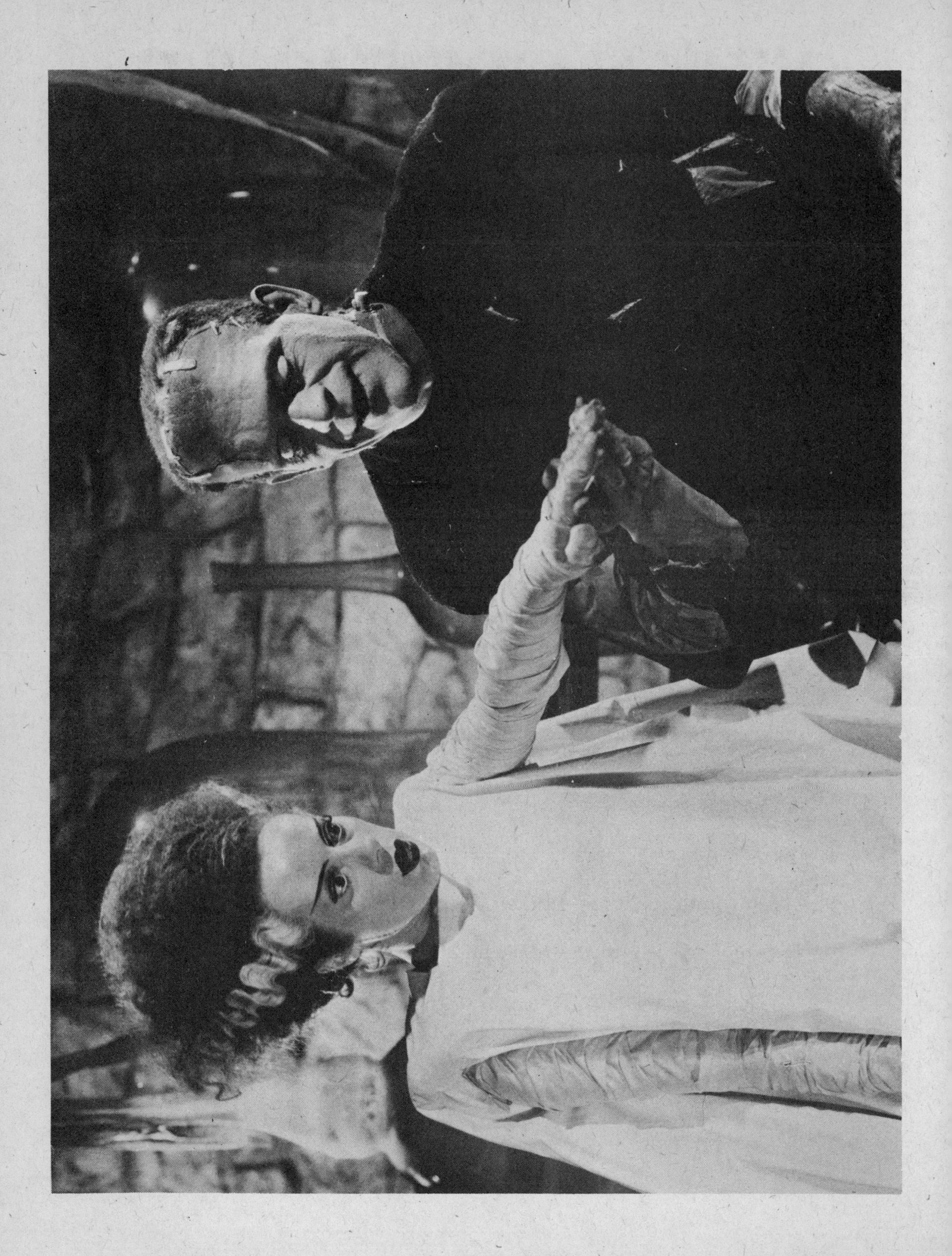

HISS AND HEARSE

Perfect couples are made, not born—usually in heaven but sometimes in a laboratory, and always when they meet, sparks fly. Even so, these two broke all records . . .

1. Who are the newlyweds?

2. Who are the stars playing the newlyweds?

3. Name the movie.

4. This sentimental horror classic was based on a novel by the bride of an English poet. Name her, name him.

5. In the film's prologue, another poet discusses good and evil with the bride. Name the friend. And can you remember who plays each role?

6. What are the lovers saying in this photograph?

7. In what Mel Brooks film does Madeleine Kahn dress up like the lady in this picture?

8. Why?

9. The guy in the picture—what was his *real* (not stage) name?

10. The chick in the picture—who's bride was she in real life?

HISS AND HEARSE

(answers)

1. The Bride of Frankenstein and the Frankenstein Monster
2. Boris Karloff and Elsa Lanchester
3. THE BRIDE OF FRANKENSTEIN
4. Mary Wollstonecraft Shelley . . . Percy Bysshe Shelley
5. Lord Byron . . . Elsa Lanchester plays Mary, Gavin Gordon plays Lord Byron.
6. His first words are "Friend?" and she is screaming.
7. YOUNG FRANKENSTEIN
8. She has married the monster created by Young Frankenstein.
9. William Henry Pratt
10. Charles Laughton's

THE CASE OF THE QUICKSAND QUIZZER

If you've got something to hide, don't set foot in a Perry Mason courtroom. And if you've got somewhere to go in a hurry, don't get bogged down in this ''sinking man's'' quiz . . . .

1. What was the first Perry Mason mystery?
2. What is the strange connection between PERRY MASON and THE EDGE OF NIGHT?
3. Did Della Street want to marry Perry Mason?
4. Who played Perry Mason for the 1957-1966 TV series? For the 1973-1974 series?
5. What is the name of Perry's personal investigator?
6. What is the name of his perennial adversary, the D.A.?
7. What was THE CASE OF THE FINAL FADE-OUT?
8. What was the unique feature of #7?
9. Who is A.A. Fair?
10. Who are Bertha Cool and Donald Lam?

THE CASE OF THE QUICKSAND QUIZZER

(Answers)

1. THE CASE OF THE VELVET CLAWS
2. The radio version of PERRY MASON was a combination of soap opera and courtroom drama. When the program moved to TV, Erle Stanley Gardner bowed out, opting to keep the Perry Mason name and concentrate on detective writing. So most of the radio cast, with new names but much the same old format, brought the show to TV as THE EDGE OF NIGHT.
3. No. He proposed and she refused—five times!
4. Raymond Burr . . . Monte Markham
5. Paul Drake
6. Hamilton Burger
7. It was the last episode filmed of the 73-74 series.
8. Creator Erle Stanley Gardner, Executive Producer Gail Patrick Jackson, and many of the stagehands had parts in the show.
9. A.A. Fair is an Erle Stanley Gardner pen name.
10. Bertha and Donald are the hardheaded detective team that stars in A.A. Fair's novels.

SILENTS, PLEASE

Back in the days before sound came to movies, it was all done with the eyes. The eyes said I love you, I hate you, you scare me. Hence the origin of the popular phrase—the eyes have it.

1. What is the only silent film ever to win the Academy Award for Best Picture?

2. Who was known as "America's Sweetheart"?

3. The first of the great movie swashbucklers starred in the silent versions of THE MARK OF ZORRO and THE THREE MUSKETEERS. What was his name?

4. Known as the "Little Tramp," who was one of the first superstars with such films as THE GOLD RUSH, CITY LIGHTS, and MODERN TIMES?

5. Movieland's first major producer-director introduced new stars and new techniques with THE BIRTH OF A NATION, INTOLERANCE, and other works of genius. Who was he?

6. The artists named in 2, 3, 4, and 5 above joined in 1919 to form what movie company?

7. Who was the great romantic heartthrob of the silents with movies like THE SHEIK and SON OF THE SHEIK?

8. Who starred in DON JUAN, SHERLOCK HOLMES, and two versions of MOBY DICK, and was known as "The Great Profile"?

9. Who's the "epic director" who made one silent and one sound version of THE TEN COMMANDMENTS?

10. Who was the "man of a thousand faces" and the movies' first HUNCH-BACK OF NOTRE DAME?

SILENTS, PLEASE

(answers)

1. WINGS (1928)
2. Mary Pickford
3. Douglas Fairbanks
4. Charles Chaplin
5. D.W. (David Wark) Griffith
6. United Artists Corporation
7. Rudolph Valentino
8. John Barrymore
9. Cecil B. DeMille
10. Lon Chaney

CAMELOT REVISITED

Even without the magic of Merlin, they cast a spell on America in the early 1960s—and for one brief shining moment, as the song goes, the world had a new first family and the White House was known as Camelot.

1. Name the nine children of Joseph Patrick and Rose Fitzgerald Kennedy.
2. To what country was Joseph P. Kennedy named U.S. Ambassador? Who appointed him to the post?
3. When John Fitzgerald Kennedy was President, who was Vice President?
4. What Pulitzer Prize-winner read a poem at JFK's inauguration?
5. Like Herbert Hoover before him, JFK made what arrangements for the salary he received as President?
6. Who was responsible for introducing Ethel Skakel to Robert Kennedy and what did they do about it?
7. What do the initials JFK, RFK, and EMK stand for?
8. Which of the Kennedy sisters married actor Peter Lawford?
9. What was the maiden name of JFK's wife?
10. What is the title of JFK's Pulitzer Prize-winning book?

CAMELOT REVISITED

(answers)

1. Joseph Jr., John, Rosemary, Kathleen, Eunice, Patricia, Robert, Jean, Edward.

2. Great Britain . . . Franklin Roosevelt

3. Lyndon Baines Johnson

4. Robert Frost

5. Both Presidents donated their salaries to charity.

6. Ethel roomed with Bobby's sister Jean at Manhattanville College. She first met Bobby when she and Jean went on a skiing trip to Canada . . . and married him in 1950 with JFK as best man.

7. John Fitzgerald Kennedy . . . Robert Francis Kennedy . . . Edward Moore Kennedy.

8. Patricia

9. Jacqueline Lee Bouvier

10. PROFILES IN COURAGE

OSCAR AND FRIENDS

How many of these top box-office celebrities have gone home with Academy Awards for Best Actor or Best Actress? Don't start till you're sure you understand the question—

Remember, we're not talking about Best Supporting, or Nominees, or Cutest Kid of the Century. So—ready, set, play Oscar!

1. Joan Crawford
2. James Stewart
3. Katharine Hepburn
4. John Barrymore
5. Janet Gaynor
6. Gloria Swanson
7. Orson Welles
8. Broderick Crawford
9. Charles Boyer
10. Sidney Poitier

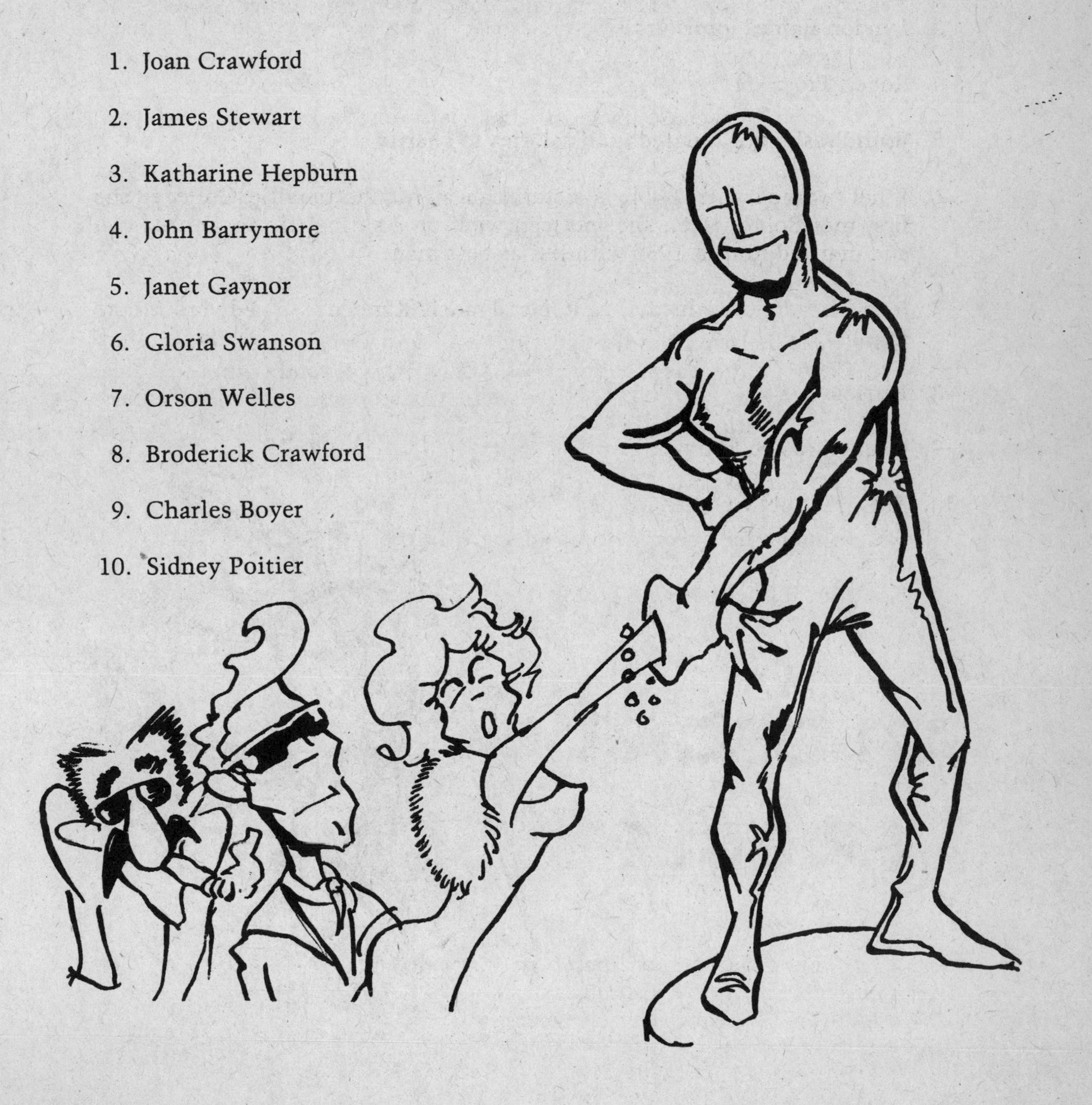

OSCAR AND FRIENDS

(answers)

1. Yes, for MILDRED PIERCE

2. Yes, for THE PHILADELPHIA STORY

3. Yes, on three different occasions, more than any other actress—for MORNING GLORY, GUESS WHO'S COMING TO DINNER, and THE LION IN WINTER.

4. No, essentially because his great films were done before Hollywood gave Academy Awards.

5. Yes, the first Best Actress award, on the basis of three films—SEVENTH HEAVEN, SUNRISE, and STREET ANGEL.

6. No, nominated but never won.

7. No, never Best Actor although he won the Oscar (with Herman J. Mankiewicz) for the script of CITIZEN KANE, and won a special Academy Award in 1970 "for supreme artistry and versatility in the creation of motion pictures."

8. Yes, for ALL THE KING'S MEN

9. No, although he's been nominated several times.

10. Yes, for LILLIES OF THE FIELD

AN OSCAR FRIBBLE

The longest acceptance speech in Academy history ran over a half hour. It was delivered by Greer Garson when she won Best Actress for Mrs. Miniver.

DISNEY-GO-ROUND

Long before Disneyland or Disney World became places on the map, Disney's movies made our heads into amusement parks and our eyeballs into periscopes, telescopes, and kaleidoscopes. If you're a true Disney fan, you'll be able to roller coaster through this quiz with your eyes closed and your brains tied behind your back.

1. ICHABOD AND MR. TOAD is based on what two beloved tales?
2. Mickey Mouse shakes hands with what famous conductor in FANTASIA?
3. Felix Salten's THE HOUND OF FLORENCE inspired which Disney movies? For which Disney movie is Salten more famous?
4. Disney produced the world's first full-length animated feature film. Name it.
5. Which film features "A Dream Is A Wish Your Heart Makes" and "Bibbidi Bobbidi Boo"?
6. According to the song and movie, of what is Davy Crockett king? Who plays the title role?
7. What Dublin-born leading man stars in THE STORY OF ROBIN HOOD, THE SWORD AND THE ROSE, and ROB ROY, THE HIGHLAND ROGUE?
8. Who gets Lady in trouble with Aunt Sarah in LADY AND THE TRAMP?
9. The good fairies Flora, Fauna and Merryweather and the evil witch Maleficent appear in which movie?
10. What substance does Fred MacMurray discover in THE ABSENT MINDED PROFESSOR?

DISNEY-GO-ROUND

(answers)

1. ICHABOD is based on Washington Irving's THE LEGEND OF SLEEPY HOLLOW and MR. TOAD is based on Kenneth Grahame's THE WIND IN THE WILLOWS.

2. Leopold Stokowski

3. THE SHAGGY DOG and its sequel THE SHAGGY D.A. . . . Salten also wrote BAMBI.

4. SNOW WHITE AND THE SEVEN DWARFS

5. CINDERELLA

6. KING OF THE WILD FRONTIER . . . Fess Parker

7. Richard Todd

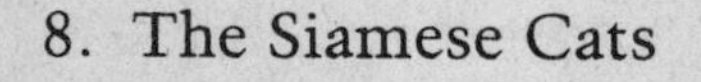

8. The Siamese Cats

9. SLEEPING BEAUTY

10. Flubber

EXTRA! EXTRA! SUPERMAN

If you go for Superman in a big way, you've come to the right place—because, in addition to this comic strip quiz, you'll find SUPERMAN: THE MOVIES and even SUPERZOO elsewhere in this book.

1. Who shrunk the city of Kandor to microscopic size?
2. Name Bizarro's home planet.
3. Who's the editor of the *Daily Planet*?
4. Who were Kal-El's parents on Krypton?
5. What's the name of Lois Lane's younger sister?
6. When not in her crime-fighting super-role, what is Supergirls' name?
7. Name the "warped scientific genius" who is Superman's foremost foe.
8. What was Clark Kent's alma mater?
9. What's the name of the imp from the fifth dimension?
10. What goes *zee . . . zee . . . zeee*?

EXTRA! EXTRA! SUPERMAN

(answers)

1. Braniac
2. Htrae (which is *Earth* spelled backwards).
3. Perry White
4. Jor-El and Lara (of course you know that Superman's name *was* Kal-El on Krypton).
5. Lucy Lane
6. Linda Lee Danvers
7. Lex Luthor
8. Metropolis University
9. Mr. Mxyzptlk
10. The supersonic/ultrasonic signal watch that Jimmy Olsen uses to contact Superman.

GLOBAL GUESSWORK

It's the same old planet it's always been, with the occasional changes made by the tides and steamrollers, not to mention the rising nations that make any map obsolete within a few years.

Well, being that Don Elmo is your buddy, I'll try not to be too hard on you in this quiz about those patches of land on your favorite globe . . . .

1. Which is geographically closer to the U.S.—Cuba or Russia?
2. Which of these is not a South American nation—Brazil, Chile, Panama?
3. What two Caribbean countries share the same island?
4. Which Caribbean nation is made up of two islands?
5. In which continent is the Vatican City State located?
6. Which of these is not considered a Middle Eastern nation—Bahrain, Qatar, Bhutan?
7. Which is closer to mainland China—Cambodia or Borneo?
8. What was Sri Lanka called before it became a republic?
9. Is Oceania in the Northern or Southern Hemisphere? What is it?
10. In what continent do you find Botswana, Burundi, Lesotho, and Zaire?

GLOBAL GUESSWORK

(Answers)

1. Russia . . . which actually *shares* with the U.S. a boundary running through the Bering Strait, just off Alaska.
2. Panama
3. Haiti and the Dominican Republic
4. Trinidad and Tobago
5. Europe
6. Bhutan
7. Cambodia
8. Ceylon
9. Southern Hemisphere . . . It's the region of islands that includes Australia, New Zealand, Polynesia, Micronesia and so on.
10. Africa

A-CAROLLING WE GO

Even if it isn't the Yuletide season, just the thought of these carols may put you in a merry mood. Try it and see.

1. What did the children put on Frosty the Snowman to bring him to life?
2. Who comes dressed in her snow-white gown and tap-tap-taps on your window pane?
3. Who introduced "White Christmas" in the movie HOLIDAY INN?
4. What instruments did the angels play upon a midnight clear?
5. What sort of tidings is "God Rest Ye Merry, Gentlemen" about?
6. Whose recording of "Rudolph the Red-Nosed Reindeer" became one of the best-selling records ever?
7. What's the name of the horse pulling the one-horse open sleigh in "Jingle Bells"?
8. Oh by gosh, by golly, what time is it?
9. What will Santa Claus check his list twice to find out when he comes to town?
10. What roasts over an open fire while Jack Frost nips at your nose?

A-CAROLLING WE GO

(Answers)

1. An old silk hat

2. Suzy Snowflake

3. Bing Crosby sang it in HOLIDAY INN for its screen debut, although he had already made it a popular record.

4. Harps of gold

5. Tidings of comfort and joy

6. Gene Autry's

7. Bobtail . . . what did you think "bells on Bobtail ring" was supposed to mean—or did you just never think about it?

8. Time for mistletoe and holly

9. Who's naughty or nice

10. Chestnuts . . . although for a minute it sounded like slow torture, didn't it!

THE SCAM'S THE THING

So you think it's easy to scam your way to fame and fortune? Then just remember this hall of fame of film flams—all that brain power that could have been spent on trivia—wasted on crimes that didn't quite pay!

1. Jim Hutton's movie about printing and replacing a bundle of money missing from the mint.

2. Melina Mercouri and Maximilian Schell make off with the jewels of a Constantinople museum.

3. Inspector Clouseau takes the rap and the real jewel thief, played by David Niven, gets off scot free.

4. There goes "The Gold of Cairo"—and a real heist is made to look like the filming of a movie in this Peter Sellers flick.

5. Zero Mostel and Gene Wilder try to get rich by masterminding a Broadway flop.

6. Robert Redford and George Segal scheme to filch the diamonds from the Brooklyn Museum.

7. Peter O'Toole, Audrey Hepburn—and Hugh Griffith as the master art forger.

8. Jack Lemmon is the injured victim and Walter Matthau his lawyer—suing football—in this one about insurance fraud.

9. Michael Caine plays fast and loose with the world's silver market.

10. Woody Allen is Virgil Starkwell. His parents are forced to wear rubber noses to hide their shame.

THE SCAM'S THE THING

(Answers)

1. WHO'S MINDING THE MINT?
2. TOPKAPI
3. THE PINK PANTHER
4. AFTER THE FOX
5. THE PRODUCERS
6. THE HOT ROCK
7. HOW TO STEAL A MILLION
8. THE FORTUNE COOKIE
9. THE SILVER BEARS
10. TAKE THE MONEY AND RUN

I GOT YOU BABE

As America's ideal sweethearts, Sonny and Cher rose to the top of the charts with "I Got You Babe" and other hits. They even had a smash TV show. Then the serpent entered the garden, the couple split—Cher went on to become an even bigger star than before and Sonny . . . well, remember his appearance on THE LOVE BOAT?

1. What are Sonny and Cher's full names?

2. What is the name of Sonny and Cher's daughter?

3. What is the name of Cher and Gregg Allman's son?

4. Cher went disco on her first album for Casablanca Records, recorded in 1979. What is the album called?

5. In what year were Sonny and Cher divorced?

6. Name the two feature-length films Sonny and Cher made while they were together.

7. Cher sings back-up vocals on which immortal Phil Spector hits of the 60s?

8. They have not always performed as Sonny and Cher. What was the first stage name they sang under in 1965?

9. Sonny and Cher met while doing session work for what famous rock entrepreneur?

10. True or false—Cher never worked with Sonny after the divorce?

I GOT YOU BA E

(Answers)

1. Salvatore Phillip Bono . . . Cherilyn Sakisian La Pierre Bono Allman
2. Chastity
3. Elijah Blue
4. "Take Me Home"
5. 1974
6. GOODTIMES (1966) and CHASTITY (1968)
7. The Ronnettes' "Be My Baby," and The Righteous Brothers' "You've Lost That Lovin' Feeling"
8. Believe it or not, they billed themselves as Caesar & Cleo.
9. Phil Spector
10. False . . . They did an SRO concert tour in the late 70s.

DON'T SNITCH ON A WITCH

(Or she may make you itch)—Instead, play this quick game of which witch is which . . . .

1. Who's the evil witch in the LITTLE LULU comic strips?
2. Who's the bitty apprentice witch of #1?
3. In the movie THE WIZARD OF OZ, which witch is flattened by a flying house?
4. Which is the good witch in #4?
5. Which witch is after Dorothy for the ruby slippers in #4?
6. Name the Biblical witch who calls up the ghost of Samuel at Saul's request.
7. Name John Van Druten's play—later a Kim Novak-James Stewart movie—about a witch who renounces her powers to fall in love with a publisher.
8. Name Russ Myer's greenish witch who hangs around with Irwin the troll in the funny papers.
9. What do you call a male witch?
10. What do you call the animal through which a witch works her spells?

DON'T SNITCH ON WITCH

(Answers)

1. Witch Hazel
2. Little Itch
3. The Wicked Witch of the East
4. Glinda, the Good Witch of the North
5. The Wicked Witch of the West
6. The Witch of Endor
7. BELL, BOOK AND CANDLE
8. Broom Hilda
9. A warlock
10. A familiar

ELVIS GROOVES

THE REEL ELVIS quiz a while back was only half the Elvis picture—the *motion* picture half. So this quiz is devoted to his records and also his groovy life. Ready? You ought to be. *It's now or never* . . . .

1. Name at least one of the four Elvis songs to reach #1 on all three Billboard charts (Hot 100,Country, and Rhythm & Blues).

2. Which song, first recorded by Al Jolson, appears on several Elvis albums including "Elvis By Request" and "Elvis in Concert"?

3. What huge Elvis hit is based on the French tune "Plaisir d'Amour"?

4. What do you find on the flip side of the 78rpm and 45rpm single "Don't Be Cruel"?

5. Its worldwide sales come to 22,000,000 and it was named *The* vocal single of 1960 by Billboard Magazine. Name the song.

6. When Private Elvis Presley went to Europe in 1958, he said "The first place I want to go is Paris and look up ___________ "?

7. What are Peacock, Burning Love, Red Eagle, Mad Tiger, and Blue Prehistoric Bird?

8. Where was Elvis during the period between March 28 and September 19, 1958?

9. Who did Elvis marry on May 1, 1967?

10. What is the name of his Memphis estate?

ELVIS GROOVES

(Answers)

1. ''All Shook Up,'' ''Don't Be Cruel,'' ''Teddy Bear,'' ''Jailhouse Rock''
2. ''Are You Lonesome Tonight''
3. ''Can't Help Falling In Love''
4. ''Hound Dog''
5. ''It's Now Or Never''
6. Brigitte Bardot
7. The names of some of Elvis's concert jumpsuits
8. Fort Hood, Texas, undergoing basic training
9. Priscilla Beaulieu
10. Graceland

THE NAME'S THE SAME. SO WHAT!

In India, the common crocodile is called a "mugger." In America, the common crook is called a "mugger." Which would you rather have meet you on the street? Tough choice, huh?

While you're trying to decide, name the *un*common animals described in the following jingles. Though their *names* will *sound* very familiar, you're not likely to meet any of them on the street.

Too bad. They might scare the muggers away.

1. It's swift and graceful
(Though it can't plié).
And it shares its name
With a famous ballet.

2. It's best to step lively
Whenever you pass
This Indian slipper
Or snake in the grass.

3. No matter its age
It's always true
An old wildebeest
Is still a ___________ .

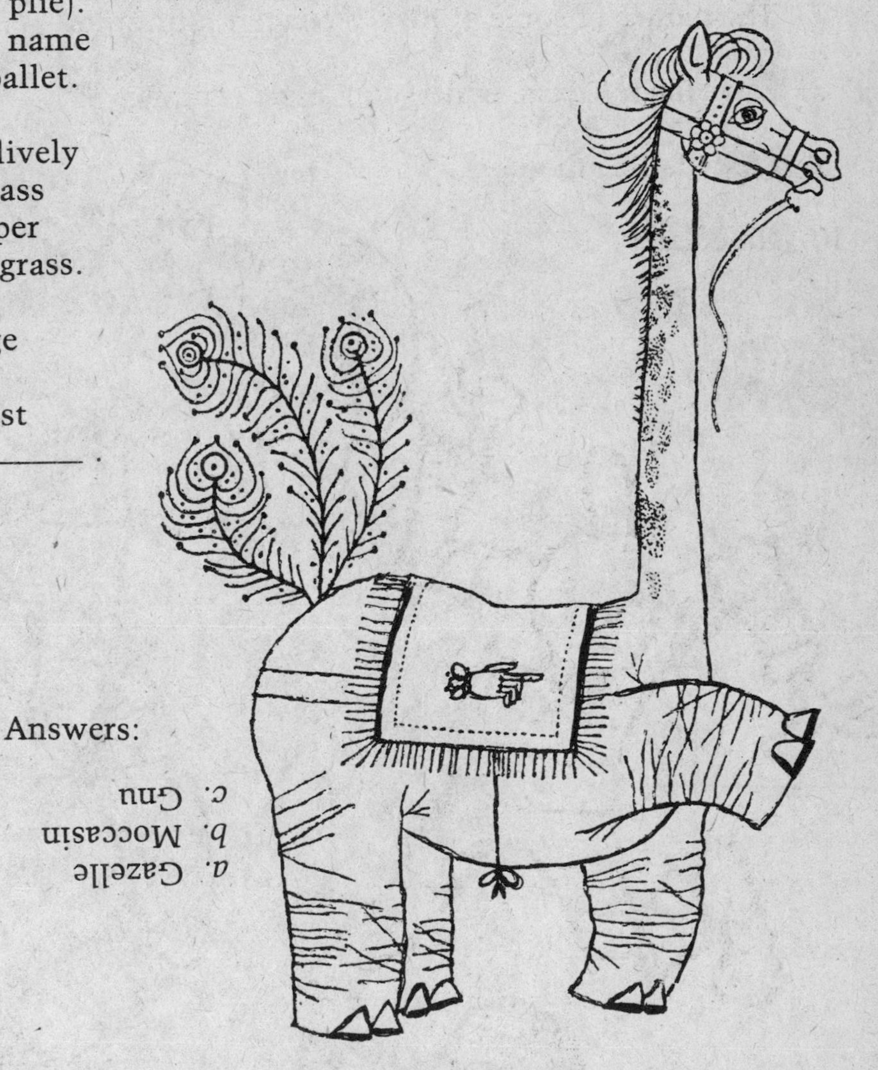

Answers:

a. Gazelle
b. Moccasin
c. Gnu

MOUNTIE MADNESS

Don Elmo here, and I'm calling you-ooo-ooo-ooo-ooo-ooo-ooo to answer true-ooo-ooo-etc, or at least, as best you can.

1. Name these stars who are America's all-time "singing sweethearts" of musical comedy.
2. Name the movie.
3. It looks like they're about to kiss, but actually, they're about to sing. What?
4. In the operatic sequence of the film, with whom does this winsome songstress sing?
5. In the dressing room sequence, who plays the silly stage-door johnny who keeps pestering her?
6. There'd be no story without the conscienceless, murderous punk of a brother she goes to the Canadian woods to rescue. Who plays the brother?
7. What comes between the lovers—until they reconcile in the last frame?
8. Who wrote the music? The words?
9. Who stars in the silent—yes, there actually was a silent—version?
10. Who stars in the remake?

MOUNTIE MADNESS

(answers)

1. Jeanette MacDonald and Nelson Eddy
2. INDIAN LOVE CALL, though it is usually referred to as ROSE MARIE.
3. "Indian Love Call"
4. Allan Jones
5. David Niven
6. James Stewart
7. Nelson plays the Royal Canadian Mounted Policeman who arrests Jeanette's brother for murder.
8. Rudolf Friml . . . Oscar Hammerstein
9. Joan Crawford
10. Ann Blyth and Howard Keel

OLD GLORY

Run it up the flagpole and salute it, fellow countrymen! It's your flag, and your national heritage goes with it. So heavens to Betsy Ross, let's go .

1. Who wrote the song "You're A Grand Old Flag"?
2. According to the poem, who said "shoot if you must this old gray head—but spare your country's flag"?
3. Who wrote #2?
4. Who wrote the military band tune "Stars and Stripes Forever"?
5. What do the stripes on the flag represent? The stars?
6. Did the U.S. flag ever have more than 13 stripes?
7. Who was Francis Hopkinson?
8. Did Betsy Ross embroider the flag?
9. Who wrote the lines, "One flag, one land, one heart, one hand, One Nation, evermore!"
10. When was the Pledge of Allegiance written and what was it written to commemorate?

OLD GLORY

(Answers)

1. George M. Cohan

2. Barbara Frietchie

3. John Greenleaf Whittier

4. John Philip Sousa

5. The 13 original colonies, later states . . . the total number of states in the Union.

6. In 1794, the number of stripes and stars was increased to 15, but in 1818 the original number of stripes was restored to represent the original states so that only the stars would represent the total number of states in the Union.

7. He designed the seals of the State Department, the Treasury Board, and may have designed the original flag, although when he asked Congress in 1781 to pay him for designing it, he wasn't paid, so he may have been mistaken.

8. The legend was first made public by a grandson of Betsy Ross. No concrete evidence has yet been produced either to confirm or refute it.

9. Oliver Wendell Holmes

10. 1892 . . . to commemorate the 400th anniversary of the discovery of America.

SINGING SWEETHEARTS

Jeanette MacDonald and Nelson Eddy made 8 musicals together. Whether you consider them "high camp" or "falling in love with someone" to music—if you can answer these questions, you can't be all bad.

1. Name the 8 movies they made together.
2. Before teaming with Nelson, Jeanette was paired with a European singing star in 4 successful musicals. Who was the star and what were the musicals?
3. Who was Jeanette's co-star in SMILIN' THROUGH?
4. Who was Nelson's co-star in THE CHOCOLATE SOLDIER?
5. In which Disney movie does Nelson do all the voices for "The Whale Who Wanted to Sing at the Met"?
6. In which movie do they declare their love with the duet "Ah! Sweet Mystery of Life"?
7. In which of their movies is John Barrymore the wronged husband of Jeanette MacDonald?
8. What was Nelson's last movie?
9. What was Jeanette's last movie?
10. Which of their movies was nominated for an Academy Award?

SINGING SWEETHEARTS

(answers)

1. NAUGHTY MARIETTA, ROSE MARIE, MAYTIME, THE GIRL OF THE GOLDEN WEST, SWEETHEARTS, NEW MOON, BITTER SWEET, I MARRIED AN ANGEL.

2. THE LOVE PARADE, ONE HOUR WITH YOU, LOVE ME TONIGHT and THE MERRY WIDOW with Maurice Chevalier (not to mention 10 films made with other leading men before NAUGHTY MARIETTA IN 1935).

3. Gene Raymond, her husband

4. Rise Stevens

5. MAKE MINE MUSIC, a sort of FANTASIA for pop tunes

6. NAUGHTY MARIETTA

7. MAYTIME

8. NORTHWEST OUTPOST (1947)

9. THE SUN COMES UP (1949)

10. NAUGHTY MARIETTA (SAN FRANCISCO was nominated the following year—Jeanette was in it with Clark Gable and Spencer Tracy but not Nelson Eddy, so if you answered SAN FRANCISCO, you answered wrong).

X MARKS THE WHAT?

If you're the sort of person who prefers *Brand X*, you should be able to identify all ten of these words and names that start with the letter *X* . . .

1. Socrates' shrewish wife.
2. A trademarked photocopying process, from a Greek word meaning *dry*.
3. Persons under 17 not admitted.
4. One of the chemical elements—an inert gas.
5. A percussion instrument made of wooden bars.
6. Mexico's picturesque Floating Gardens of __________ ?
7. The actor who played Pahoo-Ka-Ta-Wah in the TV series YANCY DERRINGER.
8. The Lionel Atwill-Fay Wray movie about a weirdo who strangles people during the full moon.
9. A Mediterranean vessel.
10. Olivia Newton-John and Gene Kelly sing and dance their way to dreams-come-true in what kaleidoscopic movie of the early 1980s?

X MARKS THE WHAT?

(answers)

1. Xanthippe
2. Xerox
3. X-rated
4. Xenon
5. Xylophone
6. Xochimilco
7. X. Brands
8. DOCTOR X
9. Xebec
10. XANADU

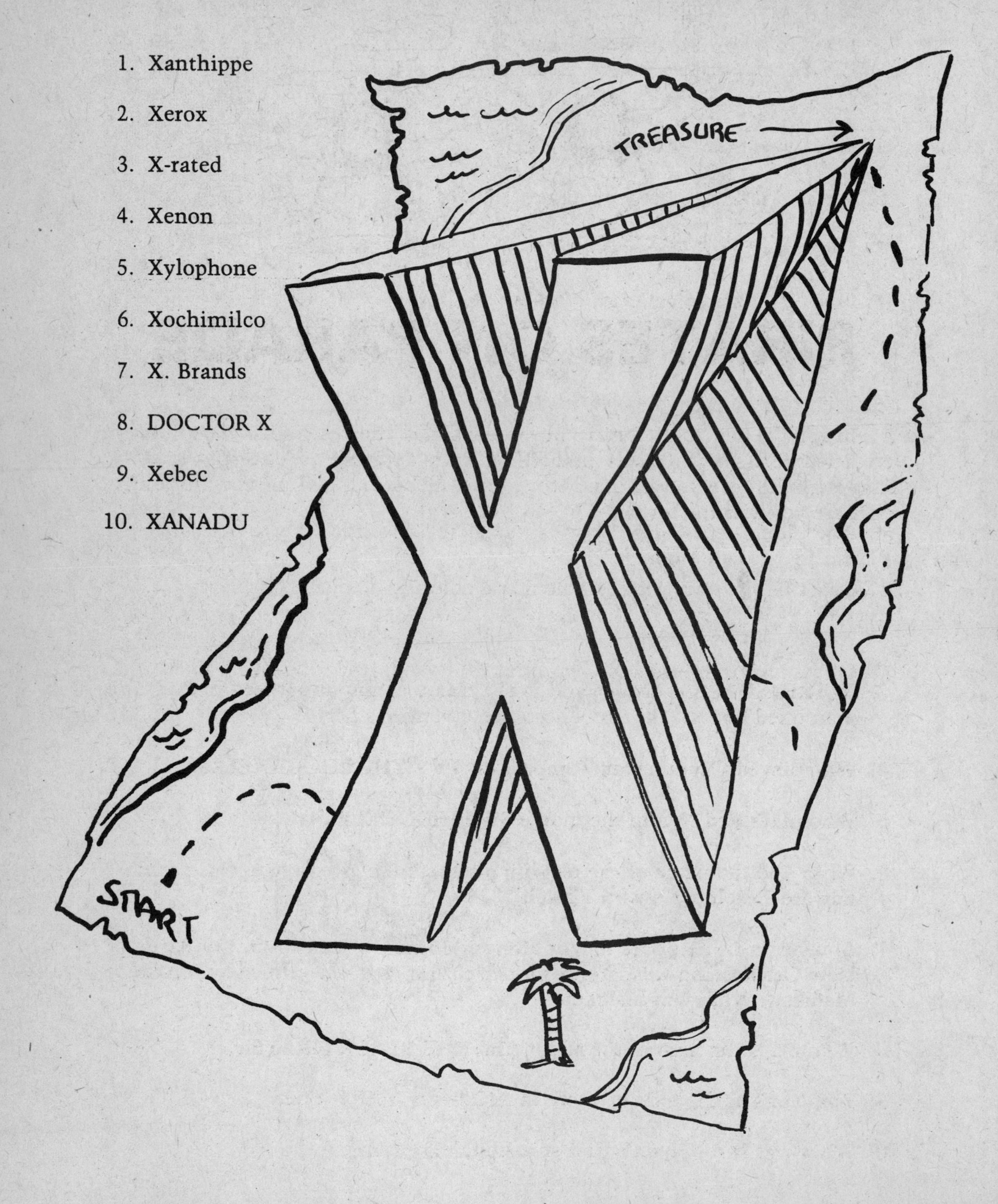

PIRATES ON PARADE

Imagine Long John Silver, Blackbeard and the rest, sitting on flower-festooned floats with coeds in bathing suits, waving to cheering crowds. That ought to give your mind a workout. And speaking of mental workouts, what are you waiting for . . . ?

1. Describe the traditional emblem and coloring of a pirate flag.
2. What was #1 called?
3. In TREASURE ISLAND, what is the name of the one-legged pirate? The marooned pirate? The inn where the adventures begin?
4. Who played Captain Dan Tempest on TV's THE BUCCANEERS?
5. Who plays Red Ned in the movie SWASHBUCKLER?
6. What was the name of the real-life pirate whose given name was probably Edward Teach or Edward Thatch?
7. Another real-life pirate fought alongside Andrew Jackson in the Battle of New Orleans and was later pardoned for his high-sea crimes by President Madison. What was his name?
8. Who plays the hero in the silent film THE BLACK PIRATE?
9. Who stars as the female pirate in ANNE OF THE INDIES?
10. What was Errol Flynn's first swashbuckling film?

PIRATES ON PARADE

(Answers)

1. Skull and crossbones on a black background

2. The Jolly Roger

3. Long John Silver . . . Ben Gunn . . . Admiral Benbow

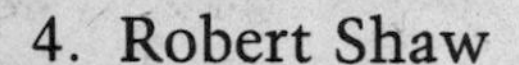

4. Robert Shaw

5. Robert Shaw

6. Blackbeard

7. Jean Lafitte

8. Douglas Fairbanks

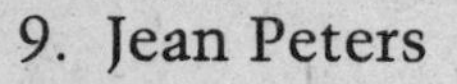

9. Jean Peters

10. CAPTAIN BLOOD

TWO ON THE AISLE

Said George Bernard Shaw, "When two people are under the influence of the most violent, most insane, most delusive, and most transient of passions, they are required to swear that they will remain in that excited, abnormal, and exhausting condition continuously until death do them part."

That's easy for him to say. But could he have passed this quiz? Can you?

1. Legally speaking, who owns the engagement ring before the wedding takes place?

2. How did the custom of the best man originate?

3. Tossing the bride's bouquet began in France in the Middle Ages, only then the bride tossed her __________ ?

4. What famous wedding occurred June 3, 1937, at the Chateau de Cande, Monts, France?

5. What two wedding customs are said to commemorate the abduction of the Sabine women?

6. What ancient people actually "tied the knot" as part of the wedding ceremony?

7. On which finger of which hand is the wedding ring worn? Why?

8. Who wrote the "Wedding March" or "Bridal Chorus" usually played when a bride walks down the aisle?

9. Who wrote the "Wedding March" usually played as she exits?

10. What is the origin of the word "wedding"?

TWO ON THE AISLE

(answers)

1. The man, although by custom the woman keeps it if the man breaks the engagement.

2. Originally he helped the groom escape the bride's father.

3. Garter or stocking

4. The Duke of Windsor married the twice-divorced Wallis Warfield Simpson, having abdicated the throne of England because "I have found it impossible to carry the heavy burden of responsibility and to discharge my duties as King as I would wish to do without the help and support of the woman I love."

5. Carrying the bride over the threshold and parting her hair with a spear.

6. The Babylonians tied together threads from the bride's and groom's clothes to symbolize the joining of the couple.

7. Third finger of the left hand . . . the left hand to signify the bride's submissiveness and the third finger because no other finger has as much trouble stretching and moving independently from the others.

8. Richard Wagner wrote it for the opera LOHENGRIN.

9. Felix Mendelssohn wrote it for MIDSUMMER NIGHT'S DREAM.

10. It comes from an old Anglo Saxon word meaning "to pledge."

ATTENTION: BIRDBRAINS

If you've stored up all sorts of useless information about birds in the recesses of your brain, here's your chance to put it to work with a quiz that might drive a non-trivia-minded person absolutely cuckoo!

1. What kind of bird does TV's Baretta have? What's its name?
2. What is the name of Batman's kid cohort?
3. Who plays #2 on TV?
4. Also on TV's BATMAN, what is Burgess Meredith's role?
5. In THE ODD COUPLE, who are the fun-loving English sisters who live upstairs from Felix and Oscar?
6. What is Robert Stroud's nickname?
7. Who plays #6 in the movie of the same name?
8. Who became Hopalong Cassidy of movie and TV fame?
9. What is the largest of existing birds?
10. This photo is from a movie about a priceless bird artifact. Name the movie.

ATTENTION: BIRDBRAINS

(Answers)

1. A cockatoo . . . Fred
2. Robin
3. Burt Ward
4. The Penguin
5. Cecily and Gwendolyn Pigeon
6. The Birdman of Alcatraz
7. Burt Lancaster
8. William Boyd
9. The ostrich
10. THE MALTESE FALCON

FALCON FRIBBLE

SATAN MET A LADY (1936) was an earlier version of THE MALTESE FALCON (1941), with Warren William as the private eye, Bette Davis as the mysterious damsel in distress, and a ram's horn (not a falcon) as the object of their search.

DIAGNOSIS: T.M.I.

What's it called when a movie character suddenly and uncontrollably begins to act brave, goodhumored, and noble? It's terminal movie illness—T.M.I. Don't expect details on the symptoms, or even the name of the disease. Nobody knows the cause of this affliction—other than to give the audience a good cry.

1. A fatally ill woman falls in love with a crook on his way to justice in the Merle Oberon-George Brent movie ___________ ?

2. Bette Davis is fading fast and her brain surgeon-husband George Brent can't save her in ___________ ?

3. The remake of #2 stars Susan Hayward and is called ___________ ?

4. Burt Reynolds seeks the aid of a therapist (Carl Reiner), a teenage-priest (Robby Benson), and a wacko (Dom DeLuise) in ___________ ?

5. Sandy Dennis takes a new lover each month until her time runs out in ___________ ?

6. Ali McGraw meets Ryan O'Neal in Hollywood's version of Erich Segal's ___________ ?

7. Greta Garbo coughs her life away and only Robert Taylor seems to care in ___________ ?

8. The operatic version of #7 is Verdi's famous ___________ ?

9. Carole Lombard thinks her days are numbered and with the help of news reporter Frederic March, becomes a headline heroine in ___________ ?

10. The Jerry Lewis remake of #9 is ___________ ?

DIAGNOSIS: T.M.I.

(Answers)

1. 'TIL WE MEET AGAIN
2. DARK VICTORY
3. STOLEN HOURS
4. THE END
5. SWEET NOVEMBER
6. LOVE STORY
7. CAMILLE

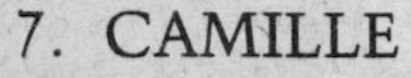

8. LA TRAVIATA
9. NOTHING SACRED

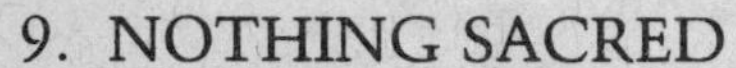

10. LIVING IT UP

ROLL THEM STONES!

If you're one of that very conservative few who think the Beatles are far-out and weird, your opinion of the Rolling Stones must be downright unprintable—which brings us to the subject of this quiz. Hint: None of the answers are ¢@*?$#!

1. What is the full name and birthdate of the Stones superstar lead singer?
2. What was the name of their tragic rhythm guitarist who died in his own pool on July 3, 1969?
3. The first song to gain them mass acclaim in the U.S., about driving a car and a man who comes on the radio, etc., is called __________? Who wrote it?
4. Mick Jagger recently divorced his wife. What was her name?
5. Mick and his wife had a daughter. What is her name?
6. Anita Pallenberg, James Fox and Mick Jagger star in a movie about a gangster and a fading rock star. Name the movie and its director.
7. On December 6, 1969, the Stones were giving a free concert when the Hell's Angels gang swooped down killing and injuring members of the audience. What is the name of the speedway where this occurred?
8. Mick Jagger sang background vocals with a woman performer for her song about vanity. Who was the woman? What was the song?
9. When Brian Jones died, what new guitarist replaced him?
10. When #9 left the band, who replaced *him?*

ROLL THEM STONES!

(Answers)

1. Michael Phillip Jagger . . . July 26, 1943
2. Brian Jones
3. ''Satisfaction'' . . . written by Keith Richard
4. Bianca Perez Moreno de Macias Jagger
5. Jade Jagger
6. PERFORMANCE . . . Nicholas Roeg
7. The Altamont Raceway
8. Carly Simon . . . ''You're So Vain''
9. Mick Taylor
10. Ron Wood

SANTA CALLING

One of the world's most famous visits is Clement C. Moore's poem "A Visit from St. Nicholas," better known as THE NIGHT BEFORE CHRISTMAS. Since it was dedicated as "a present for good little boys and girls," let's hope this Christmas bundle turns out to be your bag.

1. Where were the stockings hung?
2. What headgear did Momma and Poppa wear to bed?
3. What sort of lustre did the moon give?
4. How big was Santa's sleigh?
5. Here it comes—name his eight reindeer.
6. What did Santa wear?
7. What did the bundle of toys on his back make him look like?
8. What were his cheeks and nose like?
9. Smoke encircled his head like a wreath. Where did it come from?
10. What did Santa exclaim as he drove out of sight?

SANTA CALLING

(Answers)

1. By the chimney with care
2. She wore a kerchief, he wore a cap
3. A lustre of mid-day
4. It was a miniature sleigh.
5. Dasher, Dancer, Prancer, Vixen, Comet, Cupid, Donder, Blitzen
6. He was dressed all in fur, from his head to his foot,
   And his clothes were all tarnished with ashes and soot.
7. A pedlar just opening his pack
8. His cheeks were like roses, his nose like a cherry.
9. The pipe held tight in his teeth
10. *Happy* Christmas to all, and to all a good night!

MOON-STRUCK

What did the corny cosmonaut sing to his lunar lady?

If you answered "I'm in the moon for love," (OUCH) you might as well swallow the rest of your pride and come up with these ten titles that contain the word *moon* . . .

1. Ralph and Alice Kramden.
2. Beethoven's most popular piano sonata.
3. The first English detective novel.
4. Theme song from BREAKFAST AT TIFFANY'S.
5. Somerset Maugham's novel loosely based on the life of the painter Gauguin.
6. Kayo's big brother in the comic strips.
7. David Niven's autobiography.
8. James Bond goes after a skyjacked space shuttle. "Jaws" goes after James Bond.
9. Pulitzer Prize-winning play and a Paul Newman-Joanne Woodward movie about an odd mother and her two even odder daughters.
10. John Steinbeck's story of the Nazi invasion of Norway.

MOON-STRUCK

(Answers)

1. THE HONEYMOONERS
2. The "Moonlight Sonata"
3. THE MOONSTONE, by Wilkie Collins
4. "Moon River"
5. THE MOON AND SIXPENCE
6. Moon Mullins

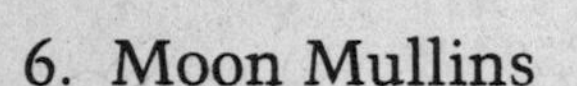

7. THE MOON'S A BALLOON
8. THE MOONRAKER
9. THE EFFECT OF GAMMA RAYS ON MAN-IN-THE-MOON MARIGOLDS
10. THE MOON IS DOWN

AUTO QUIZ

Here's an auto quiz—which either means it's a quiz you can take by yourself or it's a quiz about cars. What do you think it means? Whatever you answered, you're absolutely right!

It's both . . . .

1. What other name for car means "moving by itself"?
2. What's a wheelbase?
3. From what language do we get the words *garage, chassis* and *chaffeur?* Why?
4. In the old days, what did it mean when they advertised a car that "starts from the seat"?
5. What's the difference between a "touring car" and a "roadster"?
6. What was the Red Flag Act?
7. What's an Amphicar?
8. Before gasoline engines became popular, what powered most automobiles?
9. What came first, the Model A or the Model T?
10. If it hasn't fallen out of your car or otherwise wrecked your life by giving you trouble, what's your car's transmission for?

AUTO QUIZ

(Answers)

1. Automobile

2. The distance from the center of the front wheel to the center of the rear wheel

3. The French, because they were early pioneers in the development of the automobile.

4. If a car started from the seat, you didn't have to get out and crank it to get it revved up.

5. A roadster has no back seats, only front seats. A touring car has front and back seats.

6. The 19th century Red Flag Act required that someone had to walk in front of any self-propelled vehicle with a red flag by day and a red lantern by night. (To add insult to injury, the speed limit was 4 m.p.h. which was some 5 m.p.h. slower than most horses!)

7. An amphibian car, in other words, one that converts from a car to a boat in water

8. Steam or electricity

9. The Model T

10. It transmits the power from the engine to the axles and makes the wheels turn.

2000 + FILM ODYSSEY

Some of the best and worst films of all time are set in the future. Science fiction speculation, they call it. But as we get ever closer to that magical year 2000, are you getting just a little curious about what that "future" will hold?

1. What film set in the year 2036 is based on an H.G. Wells story?

2. Sean Connery finds himself adrift in the year 2293 in __________ ?

3. Ralph Bakshi's animated feature-length film set two million years in the future involves fairies, elves, and mutants and is called __________ ?

4. Tony Russell and Lisa Gastoni are miniaturized in the year 2015 in which sf movie?

5. With which century is Buck Rogers associated?

6. Marcello Mastroianni and Ursula Andress brush with specialists licensed to kill in the 21st century in __________ __________ __________ ?

7. John Ritter stars in the year 1998 and a 30-day telethon engineered to save the U.S. from bankruptcy in __________ .

8. Cyborgs from the year 2087 travel back in time to stop their own invention in __________ __________ .

9. This time you'll have to name a TV show—set in the year 2222 and starring Richard Benjamin.

10. On TV's STAR TREK, dates aren't recorded as we do but with a unit of time, velocity and position called a __________ ?

2000 + FILM ODYSSEY

(Answers)

1. THINGS TO COME
2. ZARDOZ
3. WIZARDS
4. WILD, WILD PLANET
5. 25th
6. THE TENTH VICTIM
7. AMERICATHON
8. CYBORG 2087
9. QUARK
10. Stardate

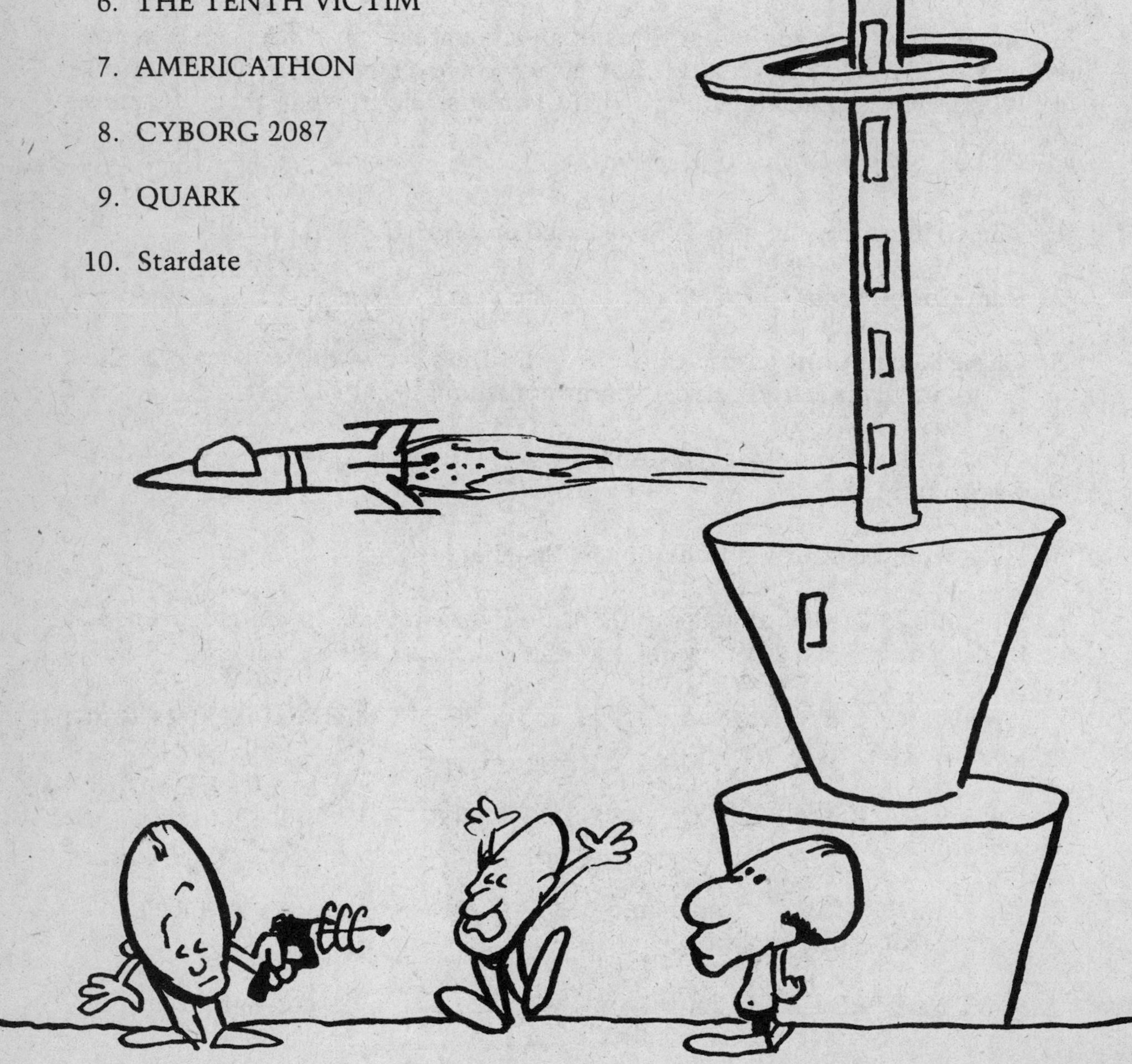

SECRET SELVES

When these dynamic dynamos aren't out thwarting crime, the world knows them as mild-mannered milquetoasts. Sometimes, mild-mannered milquetoast millionaires. Don't laugh.

You should only be so lucky!

Oh—by the way—do you know what secret selves belong to the folks listed here?

1. When not in his bat-garb, what name does Batman go by?
2. The Hulk, when he's not all green?

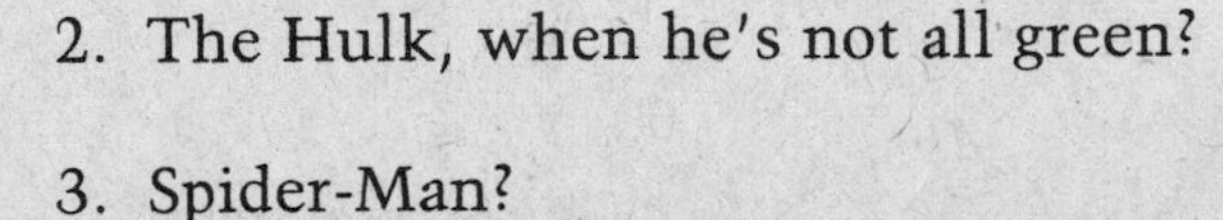

3. Spider-Man?
4. Wonder Woman?
5. The Green Hornet?
6. The Green Arrow?
7. Captain America?
8. Captain Marvel?
9. Captain Midnight?
10. Batwoman?

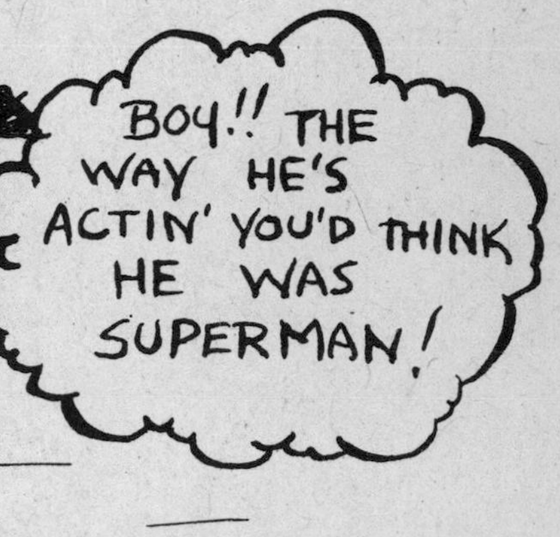

SECRET SELVES

(Answers)

1. Bruce Wayne
2. Dr. Bruce Banner
3. Peter Parker
4. Diana Prince
5. Britt Reid
6. Oliver Quinn
7. Steve Rogers
8. Billy Batson
9. Captain Albright
10. Kathy Kane

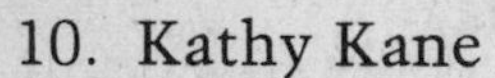

ARIA OR AIN'T YA?

Aria or ain't ya an opera fan? Watch a couple of Marx Brothers movies and some Sid Caesar reruns and you'll learn something about opera whether you want to or not. So before you tear this page out to wipe the gum off your shoe, why not see how many times you can hit the high note with these questions about opera . . . ?

1. What opera about ancient Egypt ends with the lovers being sealed in a tomb?
2. What opera tells the story of the bohemians Mimi and Rudolfo?
3. What Mozart opera is about the story of Don Juan?
4. Who wrote the music for the opera HANSEL AND GRETEL? (Trust me . . . the name *is* familiar!)
5. What opera about "rustic chivalry" takes place on Easter day?
6. What country provides the setting for MADAMA BUTTERFLY?
7. A Spanish temptress jilts a smitten soldier for a swaggering toreador. Name the opera.
8. What opera about a troupe of traveling entertainers became Gina Lollobrigida's first movie?
9. With what great diva did Ari Onassis enjoy a headline-making romance before he married Jacqueline?
10. Which opera is about the consequences of going to a costume party dressed as a bat?

ARIA OR AIN'T YA?

(Answers)

1. AIDA
2. LA BOHEME
3. DON GIOVANNI
4. The original Engelbert Humperdinck (1854-1921)
5. CAVALLERIA RUSTICANA
6. Japan
7. CARMEN
8. PAGLIACCI
9. Maria Callas
10. DIE FLEDERMAUS ("The Bat")

AROUND THE WORLD IN 80 FLICKS—SIXTH LEG

You're approaching the end of your journey. So what time is it? Time to start sending postcards to the folks back home? Time to get new film for your camera? No! It's time to zip through this matching quiz and forge ahead to the last two . . . .

1. $	a. Hong Kong
2. THE LOOKING GLASS WAR	b. New England
3. THE WORLD OF SUZIE WONG	c. Indiana
4. THE AMERICANO	d. Atlanta
5. FRIENDLY PERSUASION	e. West Germany
6. SUMMER OF '42	f. East Germany
7. GONE WITH THE WIND	g. China
8. THE GOOD EARTH	h. Brazil
9. GUNGA DIN	i. Paris
10. LOVE IN THE AFTERNOON	j. India

Answers: 1 e, 2 f, 3 a, 4 h, 5 c, 6 b, 7 d, 8 g, 9 j, 10 i.

WHO IS IT *REALLY?*

What's in a name? Sometimes everything but the true identity of the person wearing it. Suppose, for instance, you were introduced to the people named in the left-hand column. Would you know what names they go by now? Probably. But suppose you had to recognize them sight-unseen, as in the case of this matching quiz . . . .

1. Maria Magdalene von Losch
2. Krekor Ohanian
3. Allen Stewart Konigsberg
4. Eunice Quedens
5. Betty Joan Perske
6. Melvin Kaminsky
7. Joan de Havilland
8. William Claude Dunkenfield
9. Ellen Naomi Cohen
10. Alexandra Zuck

a. Mike Connors
b. Sandra Dee
c. Joan Fontaine
d. Marlene Dietrich
e. Mel Brooks
f. Lauren Bacall
g. "Mama" Cass Elliot
h. W.C. Fields
i. Woody Allen
j. Eve Arden

Answers:

1*d*, 2*a*, 3*i*, 4*j*, 5*f*,
6*e*, 7*c*, 8*h*, 9*g*, 10*b*

THE ROARING TWENTIES

With the 20s came Prohibition, Al Capone, and the Charleston. By some, it is remembered affectionately for just those reasons. By others, it is remembered for anything but. For instance . . . .

1. What did "Lucky Lindy" do in 1927?
2. Who wrote MEIN KAMPF while serving a prison sentence?
3. Who was the first woman to swim the English Channel?
4. Who wrote ALL QUIET ON THE WESTERN FRONT?
5. What event of the early 1920s was hailed as the most extraordinary day in the whole history of Egyptian excavation?
6. Who swore in Calvin Coolidge as President when President Harding died unexpectedly of apoplexy? Where?
7. Who was the first woman to fly the Atlantic?
8. What happened to world economy on October 28, 1929?
9. Who was known as the "It" girl?
10. Who wrote PRIVATE LIVES?

THE ROARING TWENTIES

(Answers)

1. Charles A. Lindbergh flew the first successful solo non-stop flight across the Atlantic, from New York to Paris.

2. Adolf Hitler

3. Gertrude Ederle

4. Erich Marie Remarque

5. The discovery of King Tut's tomb—the first royal sepulcher of Ancient Egypt to be discovered intact.

6. His father John C. Coolidge, a Notary Public . . . in the living room of the Coolidge home.

7. Amelia Earhart

8. The U.S. Stock Exchange collapsed, ushering in the worldwide Great Depression

9. Clara Bow

10. Noel Coward

GROOVY MOVIES

Take today's top pop stars, add the technicolor screen and a pinch of plot, shake, and what do you get? Well, twenty years ago, maybe you got top-pop bebop. Today, depending on how you feel about these more recent ventures, you may or may not say "you get a movie!"

1. Name the movie about the Led Zeppelin's 1973 Madison Square Garden performances.

2. Who plays the lead role in COAL MINER'S DAUGHTER? Which real-life country music superstar does she portray?

3. The Rolling Stones' unexpectedly frightening Altamont free concert is captured on film in __________ __________ .

4. Director Michael Wadleigh's three-hour tribute to the Woodstock Festival stars Jimi Hendrix, The Who, and others, and is called __________ .

5. The Who's rock opera, starring Ann-Margret and Elton John, is called __________ .

6. Peter Frampton and the Bee Gees have turned the Beatles' music into what 1978 movie?

7. What musical extravaganza marks the Village People's movie debut?

8. The film version of Jimi Hendrix's 1970 Memorial Day concert is called __________ __________ __________ ?

9. Willie Nelson plays an aging country singer who falls in love with his best friend's daughter in __________ __________ .

10. Meat Loaf, Alice Cooper, Blondie, and more, appear in what movie billed as "the story of a boy and his equipment"?

GROOVY MOVIES

(Answers)

1. THE SONG REMAINS THE SAME
2. Sissy Spacek . . . Loretta Lynn
3. GIMME SHELTER
4. WOODSTOCK
5. TOMMY
6. SGT. PEPPER'S LONELY HEARTS CLUB BAND
7. CAN'T STOP THE MUSIC
8. JIMI PLAYS BERKELEY
9. HONEYSUCKLE ROSE
10. ROADIE

THE FLIRTY THIRTIES

From the depths of the Depression came a new high in entertainment—movies, songs, and box office celebrities that were bigger than ever before. Even on the newsfront, life was far from dull . . . .

1. What gangland biggie was finally imprisoned for tax evasion in 1931?
2. What Public Enemy Number One was finally stopped by the FBI with the aid of the ''Lady in Red''?
3. Who was responsible for the flashy dance numbers in movies like FOOTLIGHT PARADE and FORTY SECOND STREET?
4. What movie won Oscars for Clark Gable and Claudette Colbert, as well as Best Film Oscar?
5. What Lakehurst, N.J. disaster was covered in the first transcontinental radio broadcast?
6. Who wrote the songs ''Anything Goes'' and ''Night and Day''?
7. Who composed the folk opera PORGY AND BESS?
8. Who wrote HOW TO WIN FRIENDS AND INFLUENCE PEOPLE?
9. Who sang the smash hit ''Donkey Serenade''?
10. What is the XXI Amendment?

THE FLIRTY THIRTIES

(Answers)

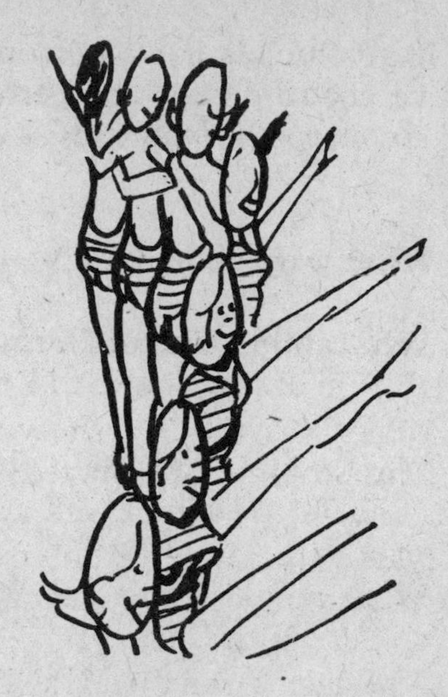

1. Al Capone
2. John Dillinger
3. Busby Berkeley
4. IT HAPPENED ONE NIGHT
5. The Hindenburg disaster
6. Cole Porter
7. George Gershwin
8. Dale Carnegie
9. Allan Jones
10. The 1933 Constitutional Amendment repealing Prohibition

CARS WITH NAMES

If a vehicle's got a personality, you can't just give it a license number. You've got to give it the perfect name. For a few cases in point—and some that are altogether pointless—solve on . . . .

1. What was the name of Pat Brady's jeep on the old ROY ROGERS SHOW?
2. What's the name of Danny's friend's car in GREASE?
3. What was the TV show that starred Jerry Van Dyke and the voice of Ann Sothern (She played a 1928 Porter)?
4. Name the Harold Robbins novel about a family of auto tycoons and the car that made their fortune.
5. What car was called the Tin Lizzie?
6. What car was called the Flying Teapot?
7. What famous fiasco car of the 1950s was named after the son of Henry Ford Sr.?
8. What's the name of the Green Hornet's limousine?
9. What's the name of Batman and Robin's unusual vehicle?
10. What's the name of the spiffy luxury auto known as the "Big D"?

CARS WITH NAMES

(Answers)

1. Nellybelle
2. Greased Lightnin'
3. MY MOTHER THE CAR
4. THE BETSY
5. The Model T Ford
6. The Stanley Steamer
7. The Edsel
8. The Black Beauty
9. The Batmobile
10. The Duesenberg

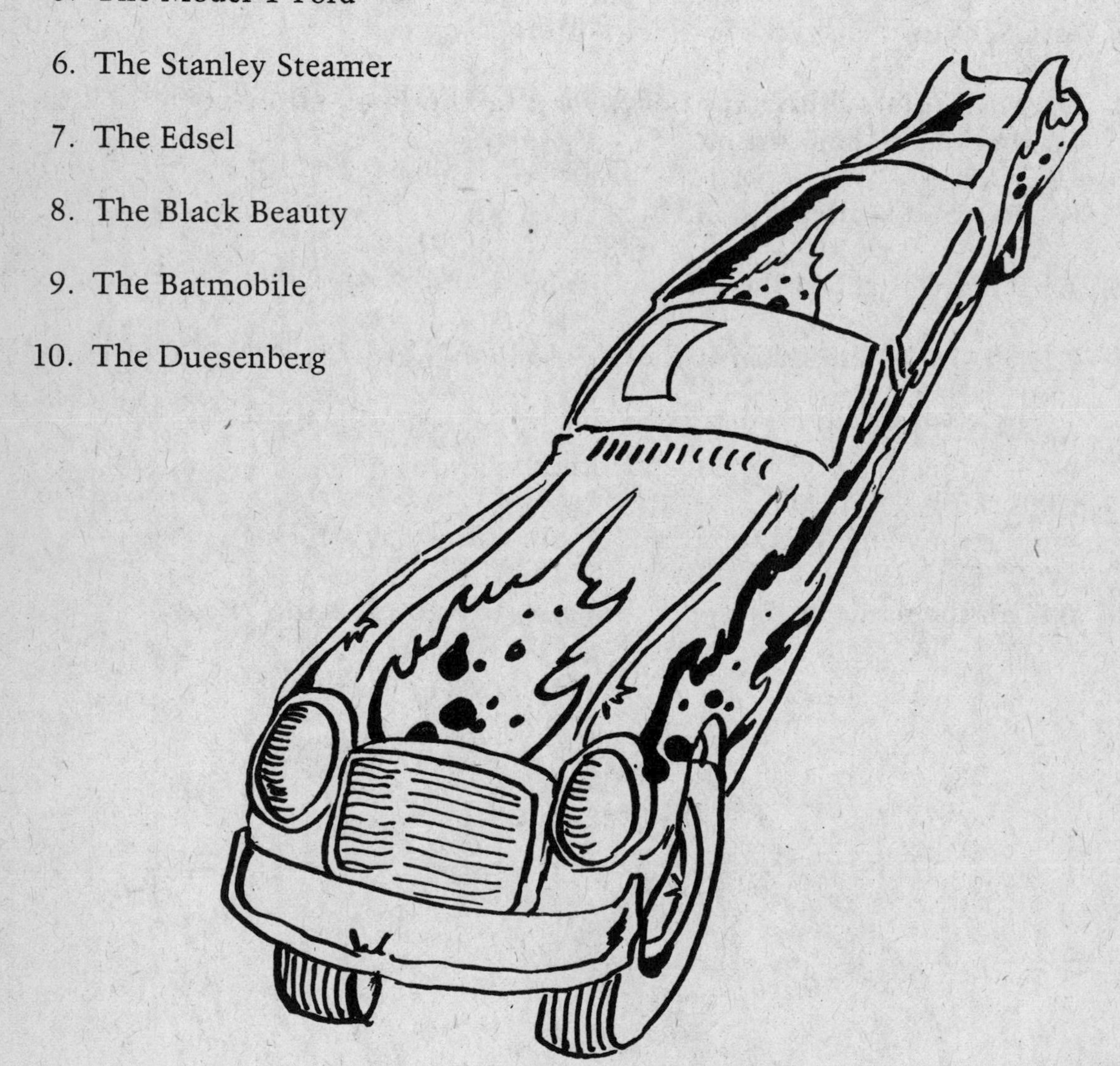

KNOW YOUR AUTHORS

With all the stories they've given us and the characters they've made famous, not only in books but in movie and TV versions of their works, it's time we gave the authors their due. Can you recognize the writers who go with each set of books listed?

1. THE THIRD MAN, THIS GUN FOR HIRE, OUR MAN IN HAVANA?
2. MARJORIE MORNINGSTAR, THE CAINE MUTINY, CITY BOY?
3. SHOWBOAT, ICE PALACE, GIANT?
4. OF MICE AND MEN, THE GRAPES OF WRATH, THE RED PONY?
5. CLOUDS OF WITNESS, UNPLEASANTNESS AT THE BELLONA CLUB, MURDER MUST ADVERTISE?
6. THE BIG FISHERMAN, THE ROBE, MAGNIFICENT OBSESSION?
7. CURTAIN, SLEEPING MURDER, ELEPHANTS CAN REMEMBER?
8. SCARAMOUCHE, THE SEA-HAWK, CAPTAIN BLOOD?
9. THE GREAT GATSBY, THE LAST TYCOON, TENDER IS THE NIGHT?
10. WESTERN UNION, WEST OF THE PECOS, RIDERS OF THE PURPLE SAGE?

KNOW YOUR AUTHORS

(Answers)

1. Graham Greene
2. Herman Wouk
3. Edna Ferber
4. John Steinbeck
5. Dorothy L. Sayers
6. Lloyd C. Douglas
7. Agatha Christie
8. Raphael Sabatini
9. F. Scott Fitzgerald
10. Zane Grey

MR. AND MYTH

If you think mere mortals have trouble with love, consider the lot of the Greek and Roman gods. One wrong move and you were turned into a rock, an echo, or a plant. No wonder you don't find any Greek and Roman gods around today!

But for old time's sake, why not match these pairs of mythical lovers?

1. Cupid	a. Thisbe
2. Helen of Troy	b. Penelope
3. Hero	c. Medea
4. Orpheus	d. Narcissus
5. Echo	e. Psyche
6. Pyramus	f. Leander
7. Pygmalion	g. Paris
8. Jason	h. Eurydice
9. Odysseus	i. Thalia, Phthia, Cassandra
10. Apollo	j. Galatea

Answers: 1 e, 2 g, 3 f, 4 h, 5 d, 6 a, 7 j, 8 c, 9 b, 10 i.

INKY FINKS AND FUNNY FOES

Take this handful of fiends and rivals and match them with—who else?—the gung-ho heroes whose lives they make complete each day in the funny pages . . . .

1. Road Runner	a. Sarge
2. Buck Rogers	b. Loki
3. Green Lantern	c. Reggie Mantle
4. Archie Andrews	d. Harlequin
5. Sad Sack	e. Ming the Merciless
6. Flash Gordon	f. Wile E. Coyote
7. Spider-Man	g. Killer Kane
8. Terry	h. J. Jonah Jameson
9. Thor	i. Dragon-Lady
10. Steve Canyon	j. Copper Calhoun

Answers: 1 *f*, 2 *g*, 3 *d*, 4 *c*, 5 *a*, 6 *e*, 7 *h*, 8 *i*, 9 *b*, 10 *j*

THE FOXY FORTIES

The 40s were as foxy as the fox trot, as funky as padded shoulders, and as fabulous as CASABLANCA and MILDRED PIERCE. How well do you know your 40s? Why not put on your thinking beanie and find out?

1. Name the actress famous for padded shoulders and her starring role in MILDRED PIERCE.
2. What century-old tradition did FDR break in 1940 and again in 1944?
3. What significant chain of events occurred on August 6, 8, 9, and 14 of 1945?
4. James Cagney played George M. Cohan in the movie ___________ ?
5. For what did Benjamin Spock become famous in 1945?
6. Who sailed a raft from Peru to Polynesia in 1947? Why?
7. Who wrote the controversial 1984 and ANIMAL FARM?
8. Who succeeded FDR to the Presidency?
9. Who was Fala?
10. What are "Mairzy Doats"?

THE FOXY FORTIES

(Answers)

1. Joan Crawford

2. He was elected to a third and a fourth term as President. Previously no man had ever served more than two terms.

3. U.S. A-bombs Hiroshima . . . U.S.S.R. declares war on Japan . . . U.S. A-bombs Nagasaki . . . Japan surrenders.

4. YANKEE DOODLE DANDY

5. His bestselling how-to book, BABY AND CHILD CARE

6. Thor Heyerdahl . . . to prove the possibility of prehistoric migration along the same route.

7. George Orwell

8. Harry S. Truman

9. Eleanor and Franklin Roosevelt's dog

10. According to a popular song of the 40s, "Mairzy Doats" means "mares eat oats."

A STATE BY ANY OTHER NAME . . .

. . . would be hard to find on a roadmap. But that's not to say we *couldn't* forget all 50 names. After all, we've already forgotten what the names mean. Or have we? A quick glance at this list will tell you for sure . . . .

1. What two states get their name from the Sioux word for *friend* or *ally?*
2. What state name comes from the Choctaw word for *red man?*
3. What state gets its name from the Spanish word for *red,* or *reddish-colored?*
4. What state was named by Ponce de Leon in honor of Easter Sunday?
5. What state was named after King George II of England?
6. What state name is a Sioux word meaning "one who puts to sleep"?
7. Which state was named after the wife of King Charles I of England?
8. Which state name is the Spanish word for *snow-covered?*
9. Which state name comes from the French words for *green* and *mountain?*
10. What is the only state named after a President?

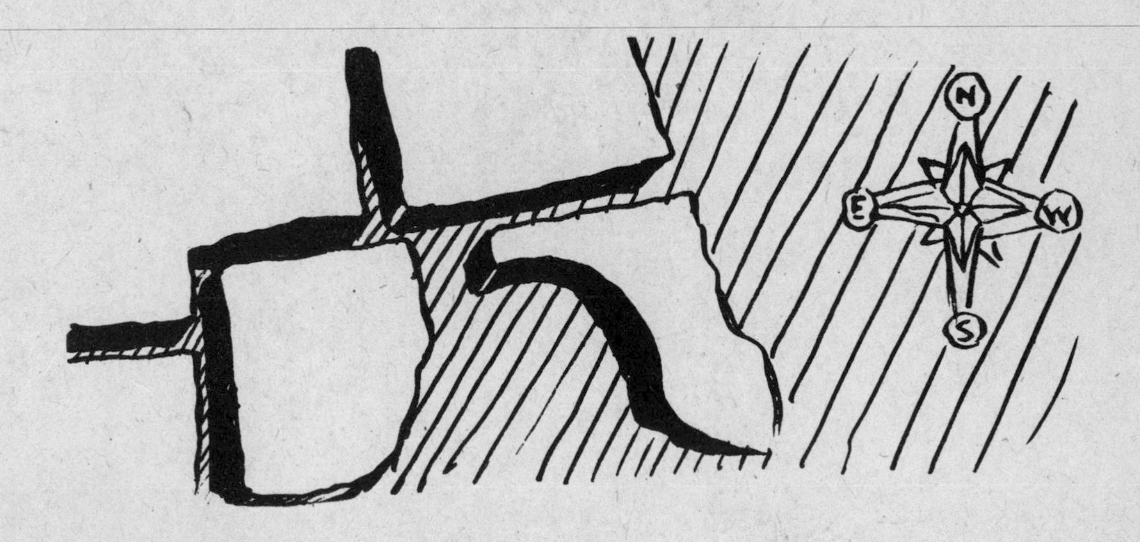

A STATE BY ANY OTHER NAME . . .

(Answers)

1. North and South Dakota
2. Oklahoma
3. Colorado
4. Florida . . . The Spanish call Easter Sunday *Pascua Florida,* the Feast of Flowers.
5. Georgia
6. Iowa
7. Maryland, after Queen Henrietta Maria of England
8. Nevada
9. Vermont . . . from *vert* and *mont*
10. Washington

THE NIFTY FIFTIES

Out went padded shoulders, in came poodle skirts. Out went World War II, in came the Cold War. Out went the old fads, in came the new ones. Only the A-bomb didn't go away . . . .

1. What Senator is famous for his crusade against alleged Communists and Communist sympathizers?
2. Who became the reigning British monarch on the death of George VI?
3. What war did the U.S. wage between 1950 and 1953?
4. Who won the Best Actor Oscar for his role in ON THE WATERFRONT?
5. Who won the Best Actor Oscar for his role in MARTY?
6. What child star from radio and early TV became a teen idol for songs like "Lonesome Town" and "A Teenager's Romance"?
7. What were the sack, chemise, and empire?
8. Where did AMERICAN BANDSTAND start and who was the host?
9. What was the *Nautilus*?
10. Who was Ike's Vice President?

THE NIFTY FIFTIES

(Answers)

1. Senator Joseph McCarthy
2. Queen Elizabeth II
3. The Korean War
4. Marlon Brando
5. Ernest Borgnine
6. Ricky Nelson
7. Waistless women's fashions
8. Philadelphia . . . Dick Clark
9. The first atomic submarine, launched January 21, 1954
10. Richard Milhous Nixon

IT'S A LIVING

For another look at real life on those TV and movie screens, take a closer gaze at what these characters do to support themselves and their families. It ranges from the ho-hum to the hoo-hah so heigh-ho, let's get to work . . . .

1. What kind of work does Mike Brady do on THE BRADY BUNCH?
2. What industry is the movie BRIGHT LEAF about?
3. What do John Wayne's HELLFIGHTERS do for a living?
4. What was Jim Anderson's profession on FATHER KNOWS BEST?
5. Who are Rob Petrie's co-writers on THE DICK VAN DYKE SHOW and who plays them?
6. Gale Storm and Lauren Tewes have portrayed the same profession on different shows. What profession? What shows?
7. What is Clark Gable's line of work in TEACHER'S PET?
8. What is Cary Grant's line of work in MR. BLANDINGS BUILDS HIS DREAM HOUSE?
9. What industry is the subject of the Rock Hudson sudser THIS EARTH IS MINE?
10. What career did Peter Lawford pursue in the TV show DEAR PHOEBE?

IT'S A LIVING

(Answers)

1. He's an architect.

2. The tobacco-growing industry

3. They fight oil fires on oil fields.

4. He was an agent for the General Insurance Company.

5. Sally Rogers (Rose Marie) and Buddy Sorrell (Morey Amsterdam)

6. Cruise social director . . . Gale Storm on OH, SUSANNA and Lauren Tewes on THE LOVE BOAT

7. City editor for a newspaper

8. Big-time advertising

9. Winegrowing (during Prohibition, no less!)

10. He wrote advice-to-the-lovelorn columns under the pen name of Phoebe Goodheart.

MOSTLY GHOSTS

For all you guys and ghouls out there,
Here's a sprite's delight,
In other words, a host of ghosts.
Take care to get them right . . .

1. What's the special name for the spirit that breaks dishes, bangs doors, and knocks furniture around?

2. In SUPERMAN, what's Perry White's favorite outburst?

3. Name the TV series starring Hope Lange and Edward Mulhare.

4. What's a bugbear?

5. What Ray Milland movie is considered Hollywood's first serious ghost story?

6. Who plays Esmeralda on TV's BEWITCHED?

7. Who's the "Friendly Ghost" of the comic strips?

8. According to Shakespeare, whose ghost urges Hamlet to seek revenge?

9. Name the old, old Bergen Evans TV show based on the word game "ghost."

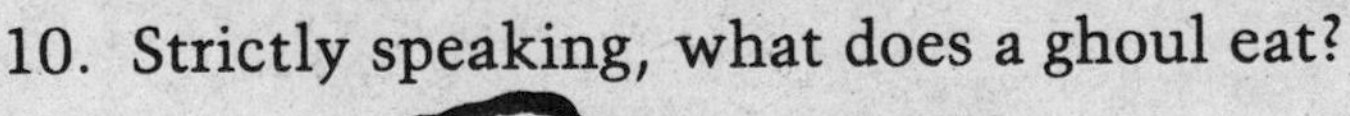

10. Strictly speaking, what does a ghoul eat?

MOSTLY GHOSTS

(Answers)

1. Poltergeist

2. Great Caesar's Ghost!

3. THE GHOST AND MRS. MUIR

4. A spook made up to frighten children and make them behave. (Let's hope there are no bugbears in *your* house!)

5. THE UNINVITED

6. Alice Ghostley

7. Casper

8. The ghost of Hamlet's father

9. SUPER GHOST

10. According to Eastern religion, it eats people, preferably dead ones.

2 FRIBBLES ABOUT EDGAR ALLAN POE

Edgar Allan Poe, the master of the macabre who wrote THE RAVEN and THE FALL OF THE HOUSE OF USHER, was buried in an unmarked pauper's grave in 1849. As soon as his relatives were able, they arranged for a proper tombstone, but it was demolished in a freak train derailment just after it was completed. Years later, in 1875, a group of Baltimore school teachers raised funds for a marble monument. At the same time, they had the body moved to a more suitable site, but not before exhuming it to peer into the coffin and view Poe's hair-raising, quarter-century-old remains.

His child-bride, Virginia, was buried in a vault during his lifetime. When it was torn down after his death, no special arrangements were made. So a scholar kept her bones in a cardboard box under his bed for 10 years until they could be buried in Baltimore alongside Poe's.

WHO IS IT *REALLY?* REVISITED

Here's another version of that ever-popular name game based on matching the stars' stage names with their given names. But if you get stuck, don't panic. You only have to go as far as the bottom of the page for your answers.

1. Bernard Schwartz
2. Archibald Leach
3. Lyova Haskell Rosenthal
4. James Stewart
5. Norma Jean Mortenson
6. Maurice Micklewhite
7. Issur Danielovitch
8. Ruby Stevens
9. Frederick Austerlitz
10. Frances Gumm

a. Marilyn Monroe
b. Fred Astaire
c. Michael Caine
d. Kirk Douglas
e. Stewart Granger
f. Cary Grant
g. Judy Garland
h. Tony Curtis
i. Lee Grant
j. Barbara Stanwyck

Answers:

1*h*, 2*f*, 3*i*, 4*e*, 5*a*,
6*c*, 7*d*, 8*j*, 9*b*, 10*g*

THE SNOOPY SIXTIES

Charlie Brown's Snoopy became the unofficial mascot of the 60s, somewhere between his impersonation of Joe Cool and the active fantasy life he enjoyed aboard his World War I Sopwith Camel.

If you and Snoopy can come down out of the clouds long enough, why not take a spin with this 60s I.Q. quiz?

1. What symbol of the Cold War was erected in 1961?
2. For what "first" was Michael De Bakey noted in 1966?
3. What did Red China explode on June 17, 1967?
4. What were the Watusi, Frug, Monkey, and Funky Chicken?
5. Who won Best Actress Oscar for her role in TWO WOMEN?
6. What movie won Best Supporting Oscars for George Chakiris and Rita Moreno?
7. Who was Yuri Gagarin?
8. Who wrote THE LAST UNICORN?
9. Who wrote PLAZA SUITE?
10. Who was Twiggy?

THE SNOOPY SIXTIES

(Answers)

1. The Berlin Wall
2. He successfully implanted the first artificial heart in a human being.
3. Its first hydrogen bomb
4. Variations of the dance craze of the 60s, the Twist
5. Sophia Loren
6. WEST SIDE STORY
7. A Russian cosmonaut and the first man to orbit the Earth
8. Peter Beagle
9. Neil Simon
10. The incredibly popular model who measured 32-22-32, otherwise known as Leslie Hornby

SEE AMERICA FIRST

You don't have to cross an ocean to see landmarks galore. The U.S. of A. has got them in all shapes and sizes, from natural wonderlands to wonders of human genius. Sure, you've heard about them, and seen photos too, but would you know where to go looking for . . . .

1. The Liberty Bell?
2. Old Faithful?
3. Bunker Hill?
4. Disneyland?
5. Vieux Carre?
6. Telegraph Hill?
7. Space Needle?
8. Smithsonian Institution (*not* Institute)
9. Monticello?
10. Astrodome?

SEE AMERICA FIRST

(Answers)

1. Philadelphia, Pennsylvania
2. Yellowstone National Park, Wyoming
3. Boston, Massachusetts
4. Anaheim, California
5. New Orleans, Louisiana
6. San Francisco, California
7. Seattle, Washington
8. Washington, D.C.
9. Charlottesville, Virginia
10. Houston, Texas

THE SKYLAB SEVENTIES

Remember the fun when Skylab turned us into Chicken Littles waiting for the sky to fall in . . . or the good times we had discovering the "me" decade, otherwise known as the Surly 70s?

Don't worry. You may have hated them first time around, but in a few years, you'll even be nostalgic about . . . .

1. Who was the multi-millionaire's daughter kidnapped by the Symbionese Liberation Army?
2. A 1970 bill signed by President Nixon lowered the voting age in national elections from __________ to __________ ?
3. Toga parties swept the nation thanks to the National Lampoon movie __________ ?
4. Who became the first American world chess champ in 1972?
5. What became of Karol Cardinal Wojtyla of Poland?
6. What was banned from U.S. television in 1971?
7. Who won the Best Actor Oscar for his role in HARRY AND TONTO?
8. Who was the creator of DOONESBURY?
9. Who wrote GRAVITY'S RAINBOW?
10. What are the Tasadays?

THE SKYLAB SEVENTIES

(Answers)

1. Patricia Hearst
2. 21 to 18
3. ANIMAL HOUSE
4. Bobby Fischer
5. He became Pope John Paul II
6. Cigarette commercials
7. Art Carney
8. Garry Trudeau
9. Thomas Pynchon
10. A Stone Age tribe discovered still living in caves in the Philippines in 1972

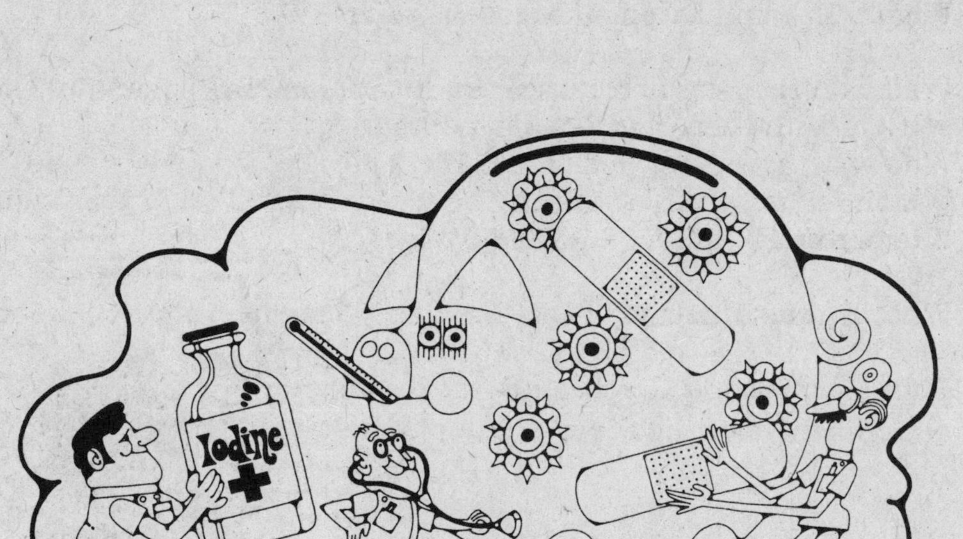

POW-WOW AND HOW!

You don't have to be Chief Legal Eagle to earn your feathers in this trial of your knowledge of Indian lore.

And if you've just about had it with bad puns like that one and want to go on the warpath, I have a better idea—Sioux me . . . .

1. Complete this advice given to Hubert Humphrey by an American Indian from New Mexico: "Be careful in revising those immigration laws of yours. We ___________ ___________ ___________ ___________ ."
2. What was the name of the father of Pocahontas?
3. Which Indian maiden married John Rolfe, the first Englishman to plant and cure tobacco?
4. Who played THE LONE RANGER's faithful Indian companion Tonto?
5. In different Indian tongues, *sachem* and *sagamore* both meant _________ ?
6. Who was the leader of the Wampanoag who made a peace with the Pilgrims and put his mark to their treaty?
7. Which Pawtuxet Indian traveled to and from England and helped the settlers with their planting and fishing?
8. Which Indian woman joined the Lewis and Clark Expedition as their interpreter and guide?
9. What is the homeland of the Cherokee, Shawnee, and Creek Indians?
10. Both Cochise and Geronimo were leaders of which band of which larger group of Indians?

POW-WOW AND HOW!

(Answers)

1. " . . . got careless with ours."
2. Powhatan
3. Pocahontas
4. Jay Silverheels
5. Chief
6. Massasoit
7. Squanto
8. Sacajawea
9. The Southeastern U.S.
10. Chiricahua . . . Apache

BIG WHEELS

Each year, Detroit teams up with Madison Avenue to create new names and new images to go with their newest breed of cars. All this is wasted, of course, if you don't remember Thing Number One about any of it.

However, you can make some multi-million-dollar executives very happy by naming the manufacturer responsible for each of these classy conveyances . . . .

1. Skylark
2. Thunderbird
3. Volare
4. Dasher
5. Le Car
6. Delta 88
7. Aspen
8. Caprice
9. Le Baron
10. Strada

BIG WHEELS

(Answers)

1. Buick
2. Ford
3. Plymouth
4. Volkswagen
5. Renault
6. Oldsmobile
7. Dodge
8. Chevrolet
9. Chrysler
10. Fiat

MYTHED AGAIN

With so many Greek and Roman gods in the sky, it was a bad idea to ruffle their feathers—as any of these hapless chaps can tell you.

(Do you think any of them were a case of myth-taken identity?)

1. Who was permitted to rescue his lady from the underworld, but lost her when he looked back too soon?

2. Apollo gave Cassandra the gift of prophecy, then did what when she wouldn't return his love?

3. Who was punished for falling in love with his own reflection in a pool?

4. Who is eternally punished by forever pushing a rock up a hill which it keeps rolling down?

5. Who was punished by the Olympian gods because he brought the secret of fire to mortal man?

6. Who prayed for and received the golden touch, which became a curse when even his food turned to gold?

7. What god has to bear the world on his shoulders because he waged war with Zeus?

8. Who was the Greek god of war? Roman?

9. Why did Oedipus blind himself? Why did his wife Jocasta hang herself?

10. Who was the Norse goddess of the underworld, with a face that was half human, half blank?

MYTHED AGAIN

(Answers)

1. Orpheus

2. He fixed it so no one would ever believe her.

3. Narcissus

4. Sisyphus

5. Prometheus

6. King Midas

7. Atlas

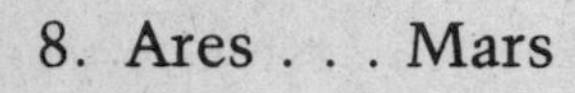

8. Ares . . . Mars

9. It was discovered he had killed his father and married his mother.

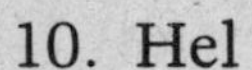

10. Hel

SKY SIGNS

Some 2000 years ago, in the time of the astronomer Hipparchus, 12 constellations loomed into view and became the Zodiac. Though the signs don't appear in the same position in the skies that they did then, they're still the Zodiac.

This only goes to prove—once a goat, always a goat . . . .

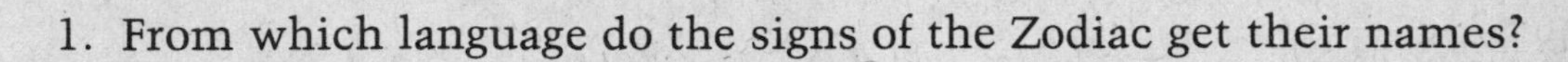

1. From which language do the signs of the Zodiac get their names?
2. What is the sign of the Lion called?
3. What is the sign of the Archer called?
4. What is the sign of the Water-Bearer called?
5. What is the sign of the Goat called?
6. What is the sign of the Ram called?
7. What is your sign if your birthday is September 20?
8. What is your sign if your birthday is July 4?
9. What is your sign if your birthday is May 18?
10. What is your sign if your birthday is December 6?

SKY SIGNS

(Answers)

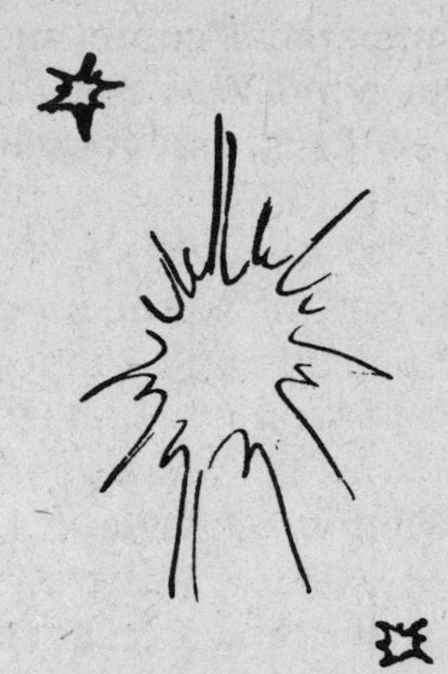

1. Latin
2. Leo
3. Sagittarius
4. Aquarius
5. Capricornus or Capricorn
6. Aries
7. Virgo
8. Cancer
9. Taurus
10. Sagittarius

PULL THOSE STRINGS

Puppeteers come and ventriloquists go, but puppets live forever. Ever wonder why? Why not ask a puppet? Or if you're not likely to see one in the next few days, ask yourself . . . .

1. According to the story, what was the name of the woodcarver who made Pinocchio and wished he would become a real live boy?

2. Who was the singer-dancer-ventriloquist-star of the TV show HI, MOM?

3. On which TV show did you find the puppets Pinhead and Foodini?

4. What was the name of Rootie Kazootie's dog?

5. On FUNNY BONERS, what was the name of the chatty duck puppet?

6. How many teeth did Ollie Dragon have?

7. Buelah Witch, Fran Allison, Polka Dottie—which was not a Kuklapolitan player?

8. Which of Howdy Doody's puppet pals could wiggle his ears?

9. What has a dog's ears, a duck's head, a raccoon's tail, a giraffe's neck, and a hankering for meatballs and spaghetti?

10. In which 1946 British horror flick is Michael Redgrave bested by a puppet?

PULL THOSE STRINGS

(Answers)

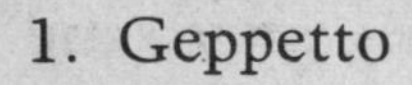

1. Geppetto
2. Shari Lewis
3. LUCKY PUP
4. Gala Poochie
5. Webster Webfoot
6. One

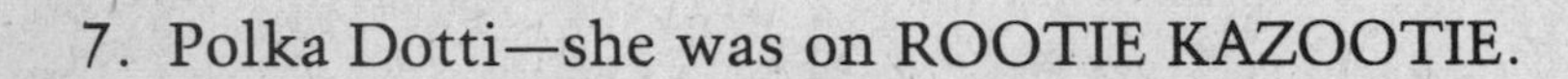

7. Polka Dotti—she was on ROOTIE KAZOOTIE.

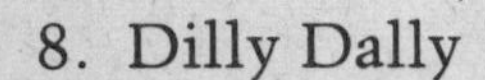

8. Dilly Dally

9. The Flubadub
10. DEAD OF NIGHT

INTERNATIONALITIES

These global travelers are citizens of the world—popular wherever they go, at home no matter where they stop—yet each was born only once, and *where* just might surprise you . . . .

1. Where was Olivia de Havilland born?
2. Julie Christie?
3. Yul Brynner?
4. Anthony Quinn?
5. David Niven?
6. Elizabeth Taylor?
7. Claudette Colbert?
8. Jennifer O'Neill?
9. Mikhail Baryshnikov?
10. Isaac Asimov?

INTERNATIONALITIES

(Answers)

1. Tokyo, Japan
2. Assam, India
3. Shakhalin Island, Russia
4. Chihuahua, Mexico
5. Kirriemuir, Scotland
6. London, England
7. Paris, France
8. Rio de Janeiro, Brazil
9. Riga, Latvia
10. Petrovichi, Russia

HARDBALL PLEASER-TEASERS

If you know your RBIs from your ERAs, you will have fun with these diamond dillies, but if you don't know where the hot corner is, these will be tough . . . .

1. What's the meaning of RBIs? ERAs? Hot corner?
2. From the years 1920 to 1925, one man led the N.L. in batting. Who, and for whom did he play?
3. Who was the only player to win the Most Valuable Player Award in both leagues?
4. Who was the last pitcher to win the Most Valuable Player Award?
5. Who holds the record for most runs batted in, single game?
6. Who holds the record for hits in a career and how many?
7. Who holds the record for stolen bases in a career and how many?
8. Who pitched in the most games in a single season?
9. What pitcher has won the most games in a career?
10. Who won the Cy Young Award for outstanding pitching in 1979 for the N.L.?

HARDBALL PLEASER-TEASERS

(Answers)

1. Runs Batted In . . . Earned Run Averages . . . Third Base
2. Rogers Hornsby for St. Louis
3. Frank Robinson, 1961 with Cincinnati, 1966 with Baltimore
4. Rollie Fingers with Milwaukee in 1981
5. Jim Bottomley, St. Louis, with 12 (1924)
6. Ty Cobb (Detroit, Philadelphia) with 4,191 hits
7. Lou Brock (St. Louis, Chicago) with 938 stolen bases
8. Mike Marshall, Los Angeles, with 106 games (1974)
9. Walter Johnson, Washington, with 416 wins (1907-1927)
10. Bruce Sutter, Chicago

A FRIBBLE

Only two major league managers have had pennant-copping teams in both leagues—Yogi Berra (Yankees, 1964; Mets, 1973) and Joe McCarthy (Cubs, 1929; Yankees, 32, 36-39, 41-43).

KELP GUZZLER PUZZLER

Contrary to ugly rumor, everything good for you doesn't taste like crabgrass.

This quiz, for example, is good for you, and it tastes a lot more like cardboard.

No fooling. But if you still refuse to swallow the "nutrition notion" whole, why not break it down into 10 bite-size bits of bafflement and dig in . . . .

1. What's another name for Vitamin B_1?
2. Vitamin B_2?
3. By what other name is ascorbic acid known?
4. What vitamin found in spinach, liver and whole milk is important for vision?
5. What vitamin found in milk, liver and sunlight builds strong bones and teeth?
6. What mineral found in dark green vegetables and shellfish is needed so the body can produce blood?
7. What has more calories, a cup of plain lowfat yogurt or two tablespoons of mayonnaise?
8. What has more Vitamin C, a medium orange or a cup of fresh, undiluted orange juice?
9. What has more Vitamin A, a tablespoon of butter or a medium-sized raw apple?
10. What provides more protein, two slices of bacon or a cup of raw oysters?

KELP GUZZLER PUZZLER

(Answers)

1. Thiamin

2. Riboflavin

3. Vitamin C

4. Vitamin A

5. Vitamin D

6. Iron

7. Two tablespoons of mayonnaise (200) as opposed to 145 in plain lowfat yogurt

8. Orange juice (with 124 milligrams) as opposed to 66 milligrams in a medium orange

9. A tablespoon of butter (with 430 IU or international units) as opposed to 120 in a medium-sized raw apple

10. Oysters (with 20 grams) as opposed to two slices of bacon which provide a mere 4 grams

DARROW'S REVENGE

You know it as Monopoly—but to Charles Darrow, an out-of-work engineer struggling through the Great Depression, selling the idea for his board game was the sweetest possible revenge. Parker Brothers first marketed it in December of 1935.

The rest was history . . . .

1. In a certain quarter of a certain U.S. city, streets running north-south are named for the seas, and streets running east-west are named for the States of the Union. This city is the basis of a Monopoly board. Name the city.
2. How many railroads on a Monopoly board? What are they?
3. What do you find in each of the four corners of the board?
4. What salary do you collect when you pass GO?
5. What is the lowest-rent Monopoly on the board?
6. What is the highest-rent Monopoly?
7. How much is luxury tax?
8. Name the two utilities. How much does each cost to buy?
9. How much is INCOME TAX?
10. What does it cost to land on BOARDWALK if there is one hotel and you don't own the property?

DARROW'S REVENGE

(Answers)

1. Atlantic City, New Jersey
2. Four . . . Reading, Pennsylvania, B. & O., Short Line
3. GO . . . IN JAIL / JUST VISITING . . . FREE PARKING . . . GO TO JAIL
4. $200
5. Mediterranean Avenue and Baltic Avenue
6. Park Place and Boardwalk
7. $75.00
8. Electric Company and Water Works . . . $150 each
9. 10% or $200
10. $2000

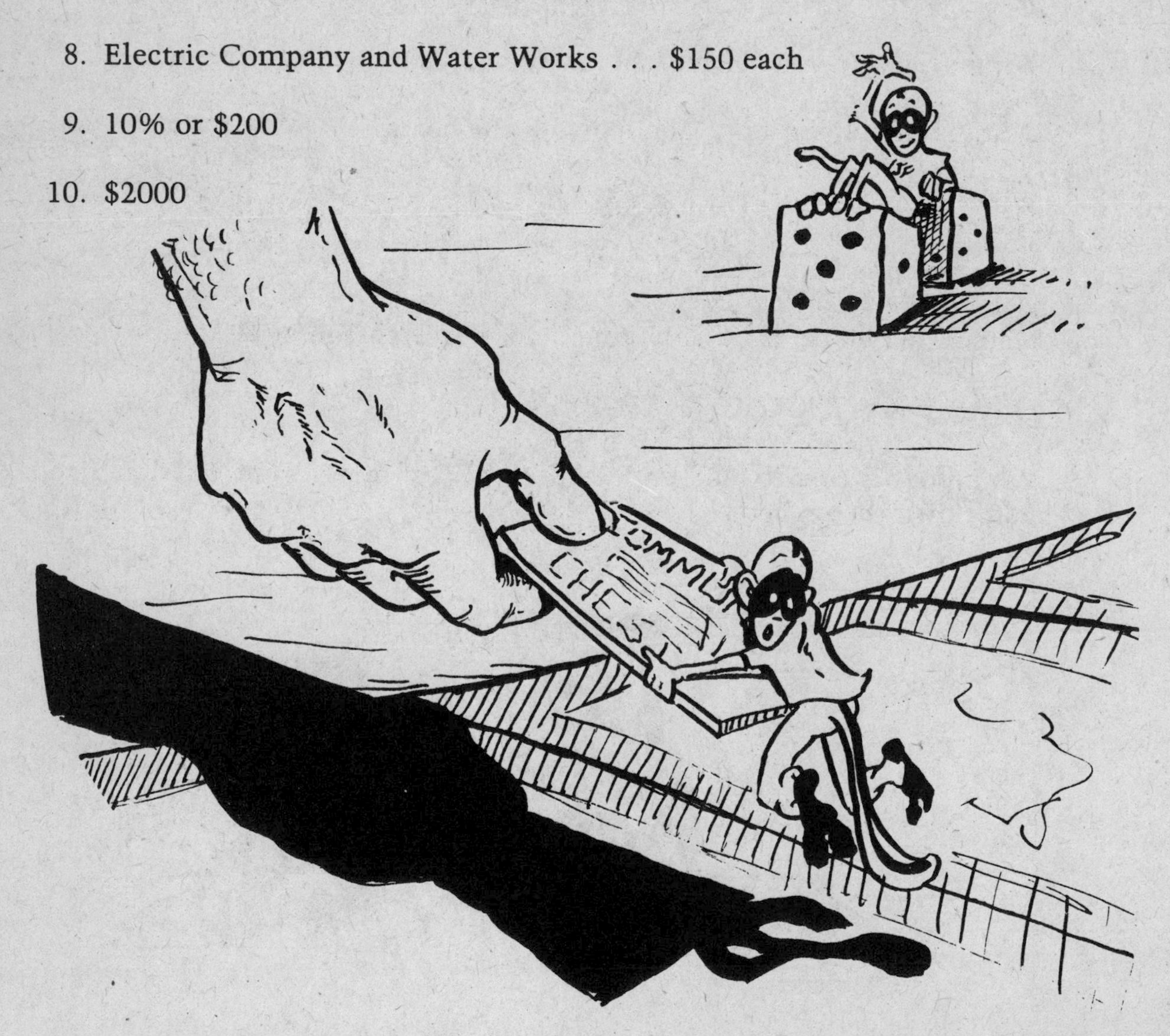

TWO MONOPOLY FRIBBLES

• The first documented Monopoly marathon was played at the University of Pittsburgh by one of the fraternities. After four days the bank went broke and Parker Brothers was contacted for help. The company came to the rescue by sending a million dollars in Monopoly money by Air Express.

• According to a 1978 poll, the fourth most expensive Christmas gift that season was a $5000 gold-and-silver version of Monopoly marketed by Dunhill.

AROUND THE WORLD IN 80 FLICKS— SEVENTH LEG

Do you realize how much laundry you'd be stuck with by now if this were an actual plane-ship-train-bus-car around-the-world jaunt? Just think of the miles we've covered with these AROUND THE WORLD IN FLICKS matching quizzes, without so much as getting airsick . . . .

1. THE BOYS FROM SYRACUSE	a. Washington, D.C.
2. ADVISE AND CONSENT	b. New York
3. THE RAINS CAME	c. San Francisco
4. NEW MOON	d. Greece
5. ON THE BEACH	e. Malaya
6. VERTIGO	f. Louisiana
7. ON THE TOWN	g. India
8. LAND OF THE PHARAOHS	h. Australia
9. CAMILLE	i. Egypt
10. THE LETTER	j. Paris

Answers: 1*d*, 2*a*, 3*g*, 4*f*, 5*h*, 6*c*, 7*b*, 8*i*, 9*j*, 10*e*

A WORD TO THE WIVES

As long as there have been marriages, hoo-hah, have there been words. Here are about a hundred of them. You might want to stick them on your bathroom mirror.

Can you think of a better way of keeping toothpaste off the glass?

Can you complete these quotes about married ladies?

1. "It is easier to die for a woman one loves than ___________ ."

2. The female of the species is more ___________ ."

3. "Women and elephants ___________ ."

4. "Whatever women do they must do twice as well as men to be thought half as good. Luckily ___________ ."

5. "A man may be a fool and not know it, but not if he is ___________ ."

6. "Early to bed, early to rise, puts you in charge of ___________ ."

7. "When men reach their sixties and retire, they go to pieces. Women just go right on ___________ ."

8. "If there hadn't been women we'd still be squatting in a cave eating raw meat, because we made civilization in order to ___________ ."

9. "Beware of marrying a person who is clever at fixing things. You'll never ___________ ."

10. And let us not forget Zsa Zsa Gabor's memorable line: "I am a marvelous housekeeper. Every time I leave a man, I ___________ ."

A WORD TO THE WIVES

(Answers)

1. ". . . to live with her." (Lord Byron)
2. ". . . deadly than the male." (Rudyard Kipling)
3. ". . . never forget." (Dorothy Parker)
4. ". . . this is not difficult." (Charlotte Whitton)
5. ". . . married." (H.L. Mencken)
6. ". . . breakfast." (Rosalie Uffer)
7. ". . . cooking." (Gail Sheehy)
8. ". . . impress our girlfriends." (Orson Welles)
9. ". . . get anything new." (Larry Harris)
10. ". . . keep his house."

THE MAN FROM I.N.I.T.I.A.L.

*I*ndicate *N*eatly *I*n *T*his *I*nstance *A*nd *L*ist . . . the words that are represented by the initials from these eight TV shows plus one pop music group and one super hero.

1. U.N.C.L.E.
2. M*A*S*H
3. S.W.A.T.
4. ABBA
5. S.H.A.Z.A.M.
6. N.Y.P.D.
7. I.M. Force
8. C.P.O. SHARKEY
9. CHiPs
10. T.H.E. CAT

THE MAN FROM I.N.I.T.I.A.L.

(Answers)

1. United Network Command for Law Enforcement
2. Mobile Army Surgical Hospital
3. Special Weapons and Tactics Unit
4. Anni-Frid Lyngstad, Benny Andersson, Bjorn Ulvaeus, Agnetha Faltskog
5. *S*olomon's wisdom, *H*ercules' strength, *A*tlas' stamina, *Z*eus' power, *A*chilles' courage, and *M*ercury's speed*
6. New York Police Department
7. Impossible Missions Force
8. Chief Petty Officer Sharkey
9. California Highway Patrol
10. Thomas Hewitt Edward Cat

*Did you remember that this was the magic word that transformed Billy Batson into Captain Marvel?

TUBE TUNES

Close your eyes and you can almost hear these TV theme songs sung by the voices that made them famous. Some are merely unforgettable, others have been million-seller chartbusters as records. But are these questions about them merely tricky, or total brainbusters?

There's only one way to find out . . . .

1. On TV's THE GREEN HORNET, who played the theme song "The Flight of the Bumble Bee"?
2. What duo made a big hit of "The Ballad of Jed Clampett" from the BEVERLY HILLBILLIES?
3. Who did "I Love Lucy" as "Disco Lucy" in 1977?
4. Who sang "Secret Agent Man" at the beginning of each SECRET AGENT show?
5. Who sang the RAWHIDE theme while the credits rolled?
6. Who scored with "Seattle," the theme song from HERE COME THE BRIDES, in the late 1960s?
7. Two records that were #1 chart-toppers in the mid-1970s came from TV shows. One was recorded by John Sebastian, the other by Rhythm Heritage. Can you name them?
8. Who starred in DR. KILDARE then made a successful record of the theme song?
9. Who was responsible for the jazz themes of PETER GUNN?
10. Who wrote "Happy Trails to You," from THE ROY ROGERS SHOW?

TUBE TUNES

(Answers)

1. Al Hirt
2. Lester Flatt & Earl Scruggs
3. Wilton Place Street Band
4. Johnny Rivers
5. Frankie Laine
6. Perry Como
7. "Welcome Back" from WELCOME BACK, KOTTER was John Sebastian . . . the theme from S.W.A.T. was Rhythm Heritage.
8. Richard Chamberlain
9. Henry Mancini wrote them, and the Ray Anthony Orchestra and later Duane Eddy made highly successful records.
10. Dale Evans

MS. DREW, DETECTIVE

Nancy Drew, detective, is a teen-aged miss who hasn't aged more than a few years in the past half-century. What's her secret of eternal youth? Now, *there's* a mystery. Oops, sorry—a *ms*-tery.

Speaking of mysteries, see what you can do about solving these . . . .

1. Who's the author of the Nancy Drew series?
2. What color is Nancy's hair in the books?
3. How old is Nancy?
4. Who's her boyfriend?
5. Who created Nancy Drew, and what else is this amazing person famous for?
6. In the movies, who starred as Nancy in NANCY DREW, DETECTIVE . . . NANCY DREW, REPORTER . . . NANCY DREW, TROUBLE SHOOTER . . . and NANCY DREW AND THE HIDDEN STAIRCASE?
7. When THE NANCY DREW MYSTERIES was on TV every other week, who played Nancy?
8. With what show did #7 alternate?
9. Who starred in #8?

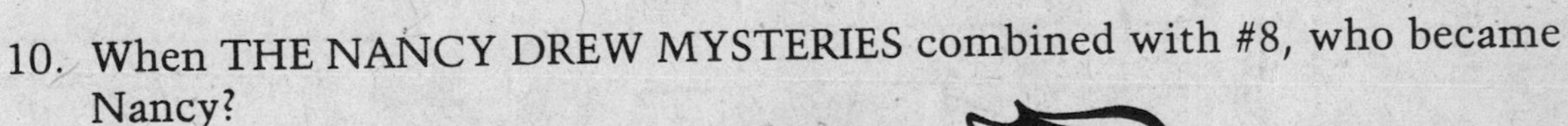

10. When THE NANCY DREW MYSTERIES combined with #8, who became Nancy?

MS. DREW, DETECTIVE

(Answers)

1. Carolyn Keene (which is the pen name for Harriet Stratemeyer Adams)

2. Blonde or strawberry blonde

3. Mostly 18

4. Ned Nickerson

5. Edward Stratemeyer, Harriet Adams' father, not only created Nancy Drew but, under some 90 other pen names, wrote many of the Hardy Boys, Bobbsey Twins, and Tom Swift adventures.

6. Bonita Granville

7. Pamela Sue Martin

8. THE HARDY BOYS MYSTERIES

9. Shaun Cassidy and Parker Stevenson

10. Pamela Sue Martin left the series and Janet Louise Johnson took over as Nancy.

NAME THE JOKER

These famous folk need no introduction. And all you have to do is name the joker who said:—

1. "The suburbs were discovered quite by accident one day in the early 1940s by a Welcome-Wagon lady who was lost."
2. "I have never hated a man enough to give his diamonds back."
3. "It's not the men in my life that counts—it's the life in my men."
4. "Yesterday I was a dog. Today I'm a dog. Tomorrow I'll probably still be a dog. Sigh. There's so little hope for advancement."
5. "If truth is beauty, how come no one has her hair done at the library?"
6. "If Charlie Chan had these clues he'd be running a laundry."
7. "Men seldom make passes At girls who wear glasses."
8. "If you can count your money, you don't have a billion dollars."
9. "If you watch a game, it's fun. If you play it, it's recreation. If you work at it, it's golf."
10. "Show me a man who laughs when things go wrong and I will show you a TV repairman."

NAME THE JOKER

(Answers)

1. Erma Bombeck
2. Zsa Zsa Gabor
3. Mae West
4. Snoopy
5. Lily Tomlin
6. Oscar to Felix (the ODD COUPLE episode where they're teammates on PASSWORD)
7. Dorothy Parker
8. J. Paul Getty
9. Bob Hope
10. Lucille Ball

FILM QUOTES OF NOTE

Watch enough movies and you'll start talking like a fabulous film character whether you mean to or not. How can you help it! The lines are so . . . so . . . *quotable!*

1. In which Great Garbo movie is she asked, ''What's the matter, Mata?''
2. Where does Ernest Borgnine say, ''Dogs like us, we ain't such dogs as we think we are.''?
3. In what movie does Bacall tell Bogart, ''We could have a lot of fun if you weren't a detective.''?
4. In which film does Clifton Webb say, ''In my case, self-absorption is completely justified.''?
5. Which film moves Paul Douglas to observe, ''One man's bathroom is another man's Carnegie Hall.''?
6. When does Bogart tell Claude Rains, ''Louis, I think this is the beginning of a beautiful friendship.''?
7. Pancho Villa's last words are, ''Forgive me? Johnny, what I done wrong?'' in which Wallace Beery film?
8. When does Edward G. Robinson ask, ''Is this the end of Rico?''?
9. When does Katharine Hepburn note, ''The calla lillies arc in bloom again.''?
10. The first words ever spoken on screen were Jolson's __________ ?

FILM QUOTES OF NOTE

(Answers)

1. MATA HARI
2. MARTY
3. THE BIG SLEEP
4. LAURA
5. EVERYBODY DOES IT
6. These are the last words of CASABLANCA.
7. VIVA VILLA
8. These are his dying words at the end of LITTLE CAESAR.
9. In the play-within-the-movie scene in STAGE DOOR
10. "You ain't heard nothing yet, folks!" in THE JAZZ SINGER

MAKE MINE MILLIONS

Join these multi-millionaires on a big-bucks trivia spree. If you're going to drop big names, these are the names to drop . . . .

1. Name the "Commodore" who launched his fortune with a ferry business.

2. Who was the richest woman in the U.S. and perhaps the world in the 1800s—known for frugal habits that included never changing her clothes?

3. Who gave away over $500 million in his lifetime—including the shiny dimes that were said to be his middle name?

4. Who said "a billion dollars isn't worth what it used to be" then died a few years later the world's richest man?

5. With RKO, TWA, and a billion dollars behind him, who became one of the world's most famous hermit-tycoons?

6. Who provided the voice of TV's unseen THE MILLIONAIRE? What was the name of his stately estate?

7. Who was the multimillionaire-swindler "Match King" who decided to own every match produced in the world?

8. Who married a Count, a Baron, two Princes, Cary Grant—and inherited a fortune begun with the first five-and-dime store?

9. Who starred as the huntresses in the movie version of HOW TO MARRY A MILLIONAIRE?

10. Who starred in the TV series HOW TO MARRY A MILLIONAIRE?

MAKE MINE MILLIONS

(Answers)

1. Cornelius Vanderbilt
2. Hetty Green
3. John D. Rockefeller
4. Jean Paul Getty
5. Howard Hughes
6. Paul Frees . . . Silverstone
7. Ivar Kreuger
8. Barbara Hutton
9. Marilyn Monroe, Betty Gable, Lauren Bacall
10. Barbara Eden, Merry Anders, Lori Nelson (and later Lisa Gaye, when Lori Nelson left the show)

FRIBBLE

Good news for the ladies—There are more female than male millionaires in the United States.

ACCORDING TO SEUSS

He once said "My animals look the way they do because I can't draw," which probably isn't quite true but who's to argue with success!!!

Besides, how can you argue with Dr. Seuss? He may have made you what you are today . . . .

1. Who or what is faithful 100%?
2. Who stole Christmas?
3. Who eats hot, sizzling pebbles from the moon?
4. True or false—Dr. Seuss used to hang around the zoos where his father worked?
5. True or false—he created TV's Gerald McBoing Boing?
6. According to the title of the book, how many hats has Bartholomew Cubbins?
7. Complete the title—THE CAT IN THE __________ .
8. Complete the title—ONE FISH, TWO FISH, __________ __________, __________ __________ .
9. Complete the title—HOP ON __________ .
10. What's Dr. Seuss' full name?

ACCORDING TO SEUSS

(Answers)

1. An elephant, particularly Horton
2. The Grinch
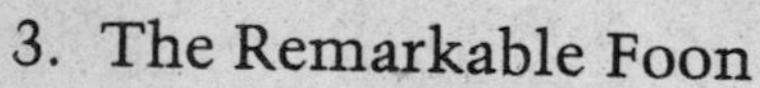
3. The Remarkable Foon
4. True
5. True
6. 500
7. HAT
8. RED FISH, BLUE FISH
9. POP
10. Theodor Seuss Geisel

MELTING POTPOURRI

You dabble in about 15 languages each day when you speak the English language. No wonder Ralph Waldo Emerson called it "the great metropolitan English speech, the sea which receives tributaries from every region under heaven"—

And he said that about a hundred years before we got some of our best words!

1. From which language do we get words like *crock, dam, knob,* and *pool?*

2. From which "invasion" of British soil do we get words like *altar, candle,* and *monk?*

3. From which settlers of Olde England do we get our *clumsy, fellow, husband,* and *bylaw?*

4. What language gives us *concerto, fresco,* and *replica?*

5. What two languages make up the word *television?*

6. Which war added *binge, camouflage, scrounge,* and *zero hour* to the language?

7. Which war contributed *blitz, fifth column, jeep,* and *quisling?*

8. You may or may not be a *parfait* fan, although the literal meaning of the word in French is ___________ ?

9. From which language do we derive *bazaar, caravan,* and *jasmine?*

10. Which language of the Old Southwest gave us *mesa, lasso,* and *mosquito?*

MELTING POTPOURRI

(Answers)

1. From the language of the ancient Britons who spoke Keltic.
2. From the arrival of Christianity to England from Rome, beginning with St. Augustine just before 600 A.D.
3. The Vikings, which is to say, from the Danish language
4. Italian
5. Greek (tele = from afar) and Latin (visus = vision)
6. World War I
7. World War II
8. Perfect
9. Persian
10. Spanish

FUN WITH LOVE

If you're not having fun with love, maybe you're just not doing right. In that case, you have nothing to lose by taking this sweetheart of a quiz. Anyhow, it's better than total boredom . . . .

1. When is Sadie Hawkins Day? What is its significance?
2. When is Leap Year and what is different about the February 29th of any Leap Year?
3. Who stars in the 1938 movie musical SWEETHEARTS?
4. When is St. Agnes Eve and what legend is associated with it?
5. Who plays the captain on TV's LOVE BOAT? What's the name of the captain he plays?
6. Before THE LOVE BOAT, Gale Storm had a TV show about matchmaking aboard an ocean liner. What was the name of the show? Of the ship?
7. Who played Bridget and Bernie in BRIDGET LOVES BERNIE? What did they do about it?
8. What is *lufu*?
9. What is the name of John Dryden's retelling of the story of Antony and Cleopatra (subtitled "The World Well Lost")?
10. In the poem "Locksley Hall," what comes after "In the spring a livelier iris changes on the burnished dove"?

FUN WITH LOVE

(Answers)

1. It falls on the first Saturday after November 11, and is a day on which a woman can ask a man for a date.

2. Leap Year is the one year in four that can only come out even if a day is added, namely February 29, on which day a woman can ask a man to marry her.

3. Jeanette MacDonald and Nelson Eddy

4. On the night before St. Agnes Day (January 21), legend says that a girl will dream of her future husband, particularly if she has gone to bed without dinner.

5. Gavin MacLeod . . . Captain Merrill Stubing

6. THE GALE STORM SHOW (in syndication, OH, SUSANNA) . . . S.S. Ocean Queen

7. Meredith Baxter and David Birney . . . the show didn't last long but they became husband and wife.

8. *Lufu* is the Anglo-Saxon word which became the English word *love*.

9. ALL FOR LOVE

10. "In the spring a young man's fancy lightly turns to thoughts of love."

THINK GREEN

If you're short on the green stuff and long on dreams of big dough, you're obviously not the Green Giant. Even so, you're not a total greenhorn if you can score a lucky seven or more on this jolly green guessing game . . . .

1. Name a sweet mint-flavored liqueur.

2. To what Scottish town do young English couples traditionally run away to marry without their parents' consent?

3. What movie did John Wayne make about the U.S. Special Forces in Vietnam?

4. What huge island was discovered by Eric the Red around 985?

5. Name W.H. Hudson's bestseller about the South American "Bird Girl" Rima.

6. Name the Errol Flynn soaper about a doctor who renounces his practice to protect the reputation of an older surgeon.

7. Who plays Gutman in THE MALTESE FALCON?

8. Whose TV roles include Ben Cartwright of BONANZA and Commander Adama of BATTLESTAR GALACTICA?

9. Who was TV's ROBIN HOOD from 1955-1958 and in all those later reruns?

10. Name the Eddie Albert - Eva Gabor sitcom about New York socialites who buy a rundown farm.

THINK GREEN

(Answers)

1. Creme de menthe
2. Gretna Green
3. THE GREEN BERETS
4. Greenland
5. GREEN MANSIONS
6. GREEN LIGHT
7. Sydney Greenstreet
8. Lorne Greene
9. Richard Greene
10. GREEN ACRES

MILES OF SMILES

You know you're an old-timer when you think of all those Americans out there who think of Donny and Marie Osmond as grown-ups—while you still remember the Osmonds way back before Donny and Marie. Either way, here's your chance to get nostalgic about them all . . . .

1. Where were both Donny and Marie Osmond born?
2. Who is older, Donny or Marie?
3. Before Donny joined the act, how many Osmond Brothers were there?
4. On what TV show did Donny make his debut and how old was he at the time?
5. When Marie joined the act, what name change was involved?
6. Name Marie's first album.
7. What was the name of Donny and Marie's TV variety show?
8. Name the four Osmond brothers who were regulars on the show. Which is oldest?
9. Who is Travis Osmond?
10. What are the names of the remarkable parents of the Osmond brothers and sister?

MILES OF SMILES

(Answers)

1. Ogden, Utah

2. Donny is about two years older . . . He was born in December 1957, and she was born in October 1959.

3. There were four brothers in the act . . . and two more who didn't perform at all.

4. On the ANDY WILLIAMS SHOW . . . He was four years old and sang "You Are My Sunshine," Andy Williams-style.

5. The name of the act was changed from the Osmond Brothers to The Osmonds.

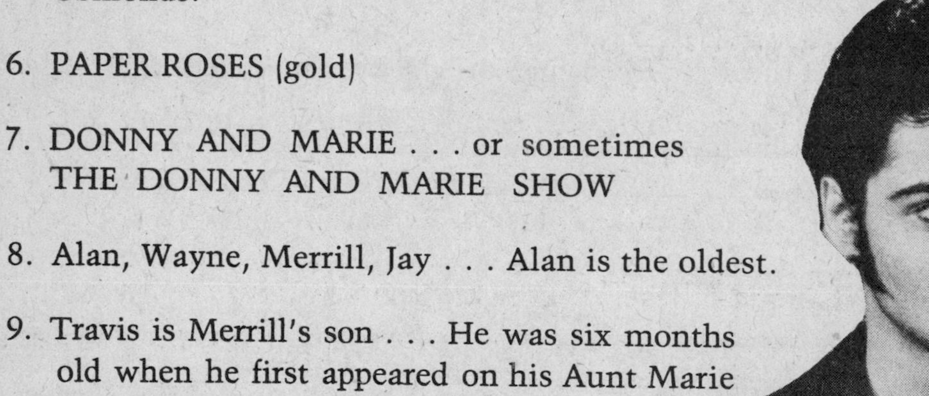

6. PAPER ROSES (gold)

7. DONNY AND MARIE . . . or sometimes THE DONNY AND MARIE SHOW

8. Alan, Wayne, Merrill, Jay . . . Alan is the oldest.

9. Travis is Merrill's son . . . He was six months old when he first appeared on his Aunt Marie and Uncle Donny's TV show.

10. Olive and George Osmond

YOU'RE A PUZZLE, CHARLIE BROWN

There are underground comic heroes everywhere you turn—and underworld comic heroes under every manhole cover. But there's only one underdog comic hero, and he's definitely here to stay. Good grief, Charlie Brown, you're a legend in your own time.

1. What's Lucy and Linus' last name?
2. Who's the little fellow who plays Beethoven on a toy piano?
3. Who arrives in a cloud of dust but doesn't say Hi-Ho Silver?
4. Who has "naturally curly hair"?
5. Who dispenses psychiatric advice for pennies when "the doctor is in"?
6. Who's Charlie Brown's heartthrob?
7. Who calls Peppermint Patty "sir"?
8. What contest does Charlie Brown enter in A BOY NAMED CHARLIE BROWN?
9. Who gets a little flaky without his security blanket?
10. Who is the creator of the PEANUTS characters?

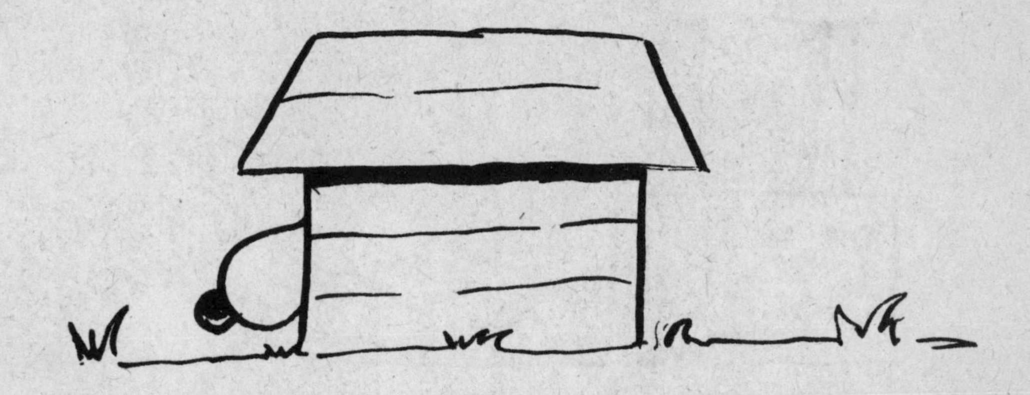

YOU'RE A PUZZLE, CHARLIE BROWN

(Answers)

1. Van Pelt
2. Schroeder
3. Pigpen
4. Frieda
5. Lucy
6. The little red-haired girl
7. Marcie
8. A spelling bee
9. Linus
10. Charles Monroe Schultz

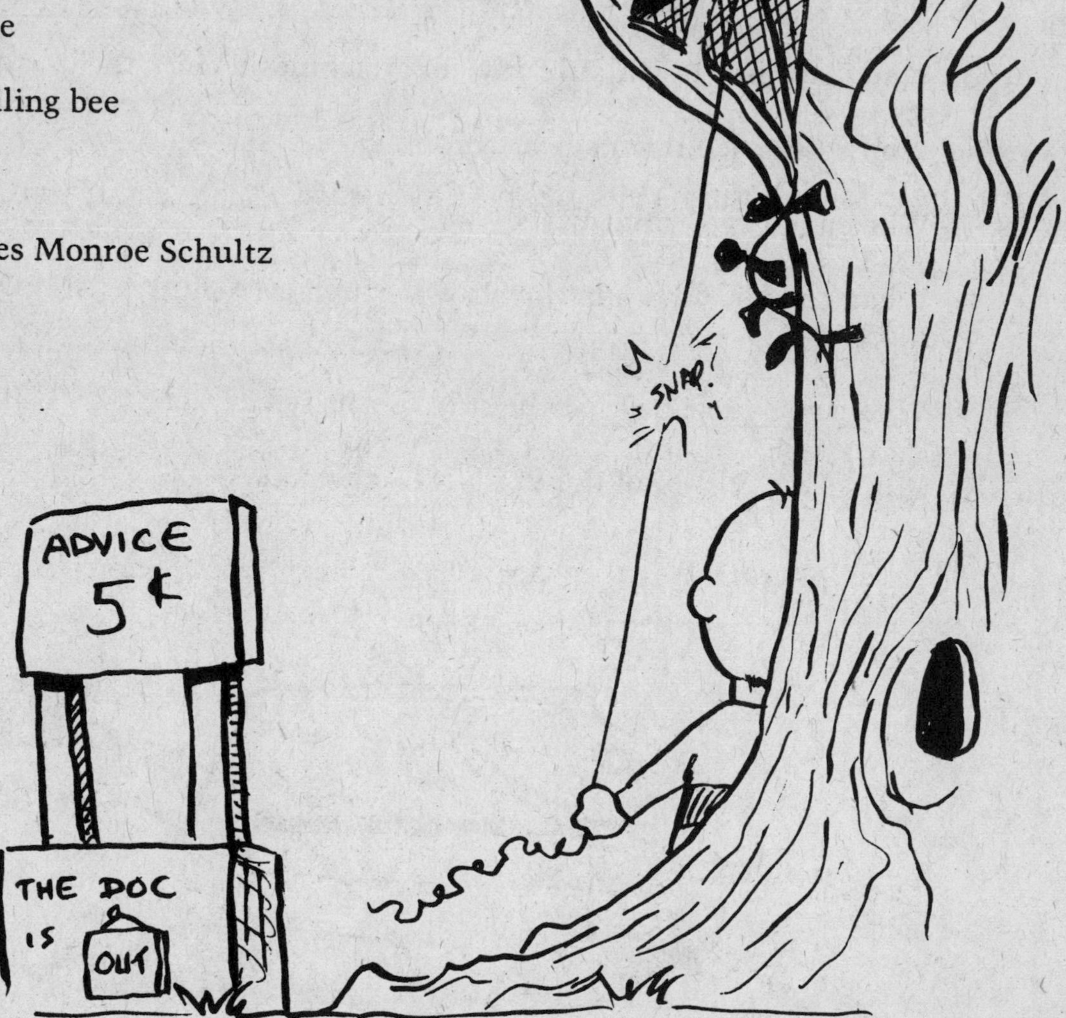

STAR FLEET STUMPER

Pick your stardate and hop aboard the Starship Enterprise with Captain Kirk and his cosmic crew. Do you know your Romulans from your Klingons? Your Vulcans from your country doctors? Your transporter room from your tribbles?

If you don't, you may find yourself stranded in deep space . . . .

1. Who's the captain of the Enterprise?
2. Who are Spock's father and mother?
3. Who's the creator of STAR TREK?
4. Who plays Sulu? Uhura? Scottie? Chekov?
5. The "country doctor" played by DeForest Kelly is named ___________ and nicknamed ___________ ?
6. What is the identification number of the Enterprise?
7. The former Miss India of 1965 is named ___________ and plays the bald, sexy Lieutenant Ilia of the planet Delta in STAR TREK—THE MOTION PICTURE.
8. The Metrons send Kirk to do single-handed combat with one of the destroyers of Cestus III, a reptilian creature called a ___________ ?
9. Members of the Enterprise crew are caught trespassing in Melkotian space and sent back to 1881 and ___________ ?
10. Spock loses his heart on an ice-age planet called Sarpeidon . . . to the beautiful ___________ ?

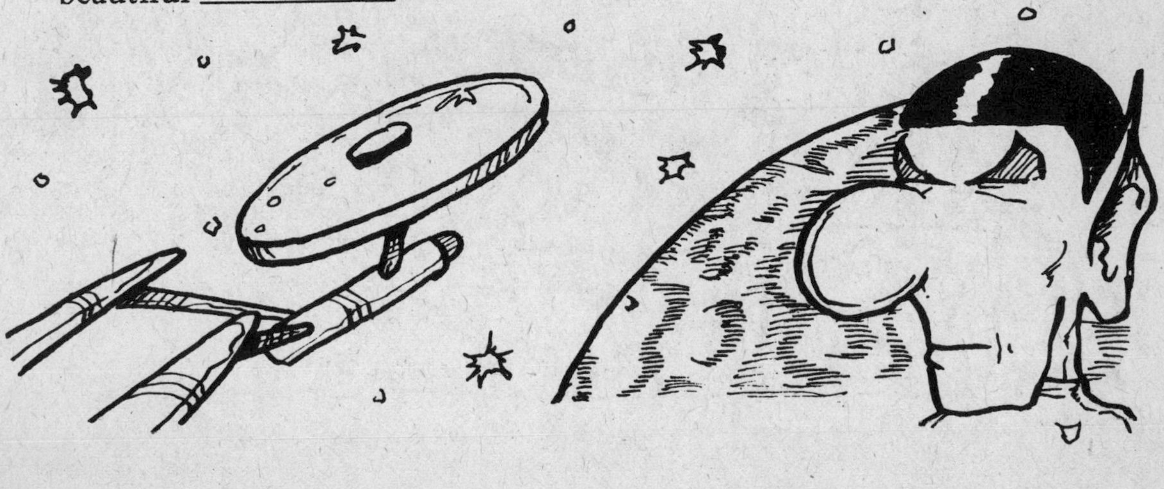

STAR FLEET STUMPER

(Answers)

1. James T. Kirk
2. He is the son of Sarek of Vulcan and Amanda Grayson of Terra (Earth).
3. Gene Roddenberry
4. George Takei . . . Nichelle Nichols . . . James Doohan . . . Walter Koenig
5. Dr. Leonard McCoy . . . Bones
6. NCC 1701
7. Persis Khambatta
8. Gorn
9. The gunfight at the OK Corral
10. Zarabeth (Mariette Hartley)

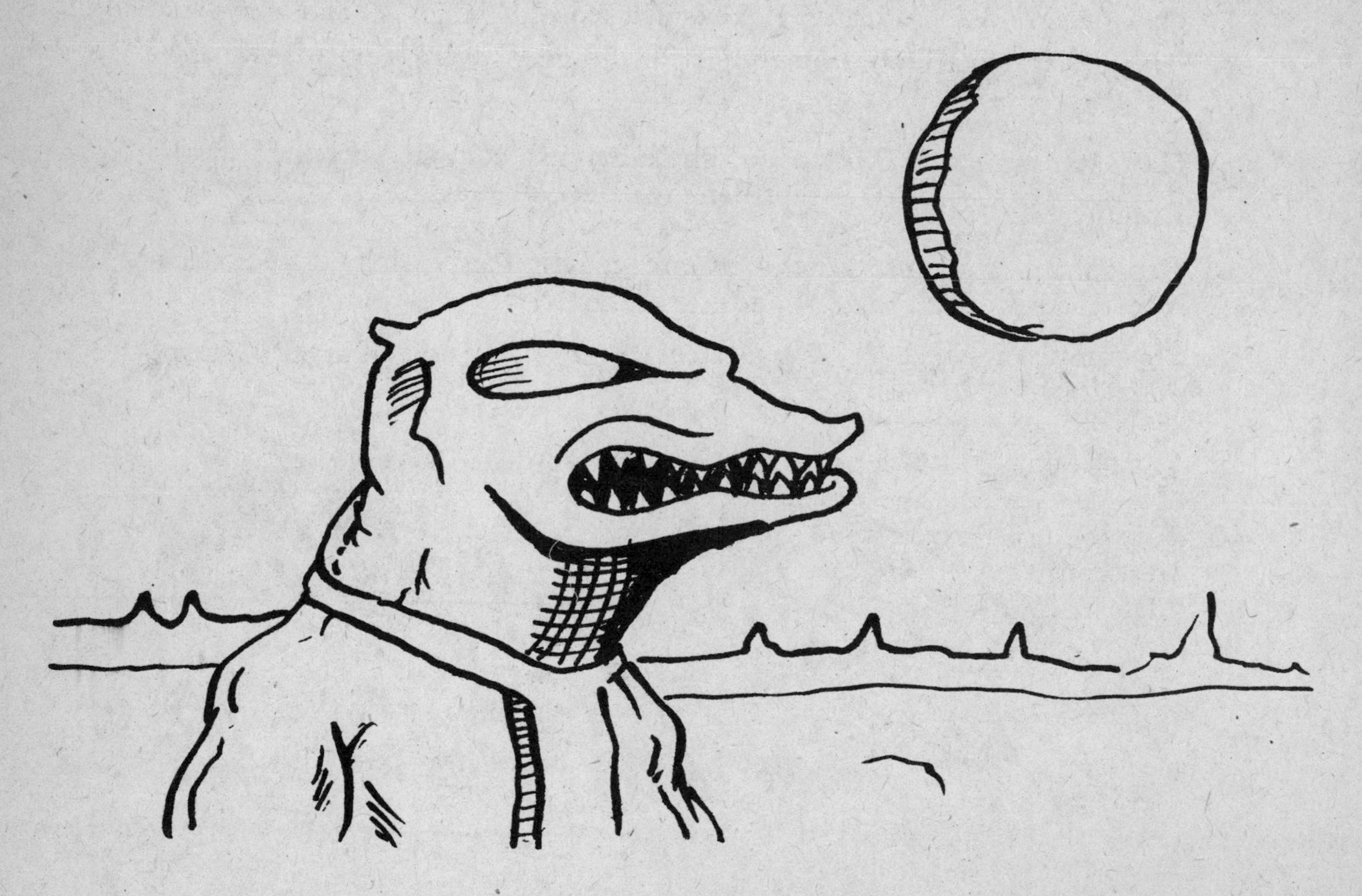

SUPERCALI-BIBBIDI BOBBIDI-HEIGH HO SONG TIME

If whistling while you work just isn't your thing (and even if it is) maybe you'd like to sizzle while you solve—by coming up with the names of the Walt Disney movies that feature each set of songs listed here.

1. "All in a Golden Afternoon," "I'm Late," "A Very Merry Un-birthday."
2. "Your Mother and Mine," "Never Smile at a Crocodile," "You Can Fly, You Can Fly, You Can Fly."
3. "Zip-a-dee Doo-Dah," "Sooner or Later," "How Do You Do?"
4. "Heigh Ho," "Whistle While You Work," "One Song."
5. "Bibbidi Bobbidi Boo," "A Dream Is A Wish Your Heart Makes," "So This Is Love."
6. "Cruella de Ville," "Dalmation Plantation," "Kanine Krunchies Commercial."
7. "March of the Toys," "Toyland," "Just a Toy."
8. "Spoonful of Sugar," "The Perfect Nanny," "Supercalifragilisticexpi-alidocious."
9. "Kaa's Song," "I Wanna Be Like You," "The Bare Necessities."
10. "Little April Shower,"
    "Twitterpated,"
    "The Thumper Song."

SUPERCALI-BIBBIDI BOBBIDI-HEIGH HO SONG TIME

(Answers)

1. ALICE IN WONDERLAND
2. PETER PAN
3. SONG OF THE SOUTH
4. SNOW WHITE AND THE SEVEN DWARFS
5. CINDERELLA
6. 101 DALMATIANS
7. BABES IN TOYLAND
8. MARY POPPINS
9. THE JUNGLE BOOK
10. BAMBI

TALKIN' 'BOUT TWELVE

What do you know about things that come in twelves? You know about months, and hours, and inches in a foot—but what do you know about the world of grosses, great grosses, and the Zodiac?

Isn't it high time (not to be confused with high noon) that we found out?

1. What's a gross?
2. What's a great gross?
3. Name the signs of the Zodiac.
4. What's a twelvemonth?
5. What U.S. Government Officer is twelfth in the order of Presidential succession?
6. The British Prime Minister lives at Number 10 Downing Street. Who lives at Number 12?
7. Which mythological strongman performed "twelve labors," including cleaning the Augean stables, killing the Hydra, and capturing the Cretan bull?
8. Article XII of the U.S. Constitution concerns presidential election . . . the right to bear arms . . . or prohibition?
9. What is Shakespeare's play about a twin brother and sister, in which the sister disguises herself as a boy?
10. Name Gary Cooper's movie about a sheriff, a showdown, and the brand new bride who doesn't want him to fight.

TALKIN' 'BOUT TWELVE

(Answers)

1. 12 dozen or 144

2. 12 gross or 1728 ($12 \times 12 \times 12$)

3. Aries, Taurus, Gemini, Cancer, Leo, Virgo, Libra, Scorpio, Sagittarius, Capricorn, Aquarius, Pisces

4. A year

5. Secretary of Health, Education and Welfare

6. The Chief Whip of the British Government

7. Hercules

8. Presidential election

9. TWELFTH NIGHT

10. HIGH NOON

SAY CHEESE!

If you have a head for cheese—which is nothing like being a head cheese—you should be able to zip through these 10 questions like Mighty Mouse through a rusty mousetrap . . . .

1. What's *whey?*
2. What are *curds?*
3. What is the leading cheese-producing state in the U.S.?
4. With what country of origin are Edam and Gouda associated?
5. Parmesan, Gorgonzola, and Bel Paese?
6. Cheshire, Cheddar, and Stilton?
7. Gruyere and Emmenthaler?
8. Limburger?
9. What's Welsh rabbit?
10. What's fondue?

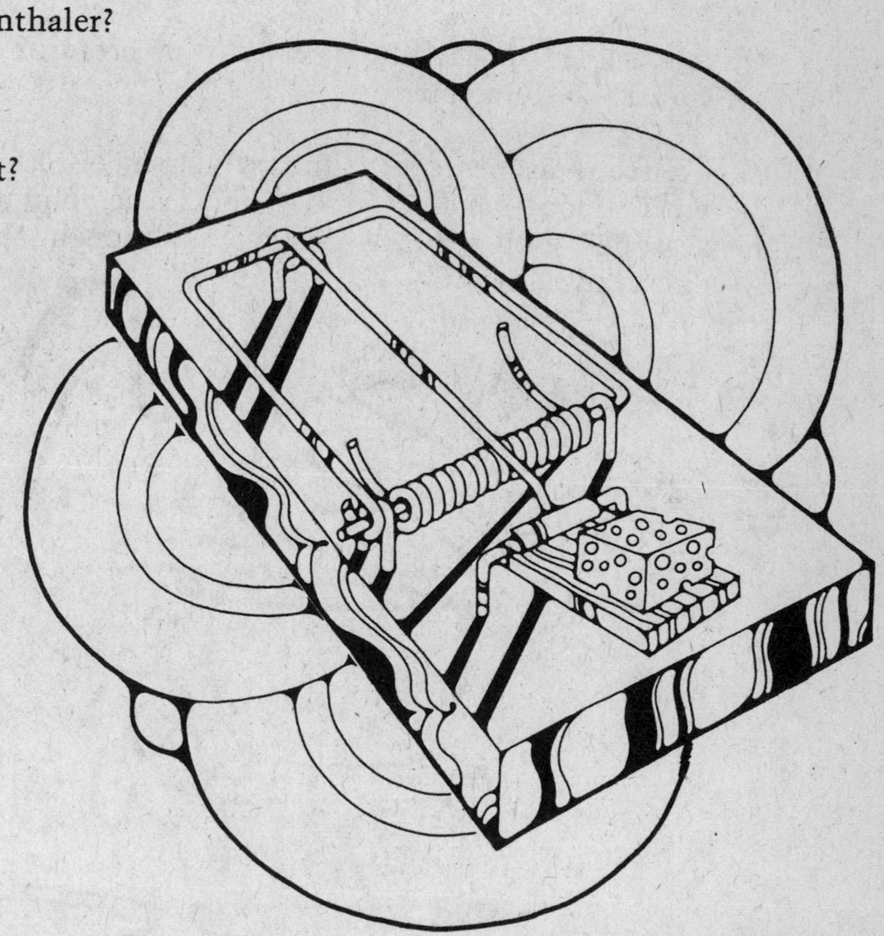

SAY CHEESE!

(Answers)

1. The watery substance that separates from milk when it curdles. The amount of whey left in cheese determines how hard or soft it will be.

2. The solid portion left in milk when it curdles

3. Wisconsin

4. Holland

5. Italy

6. England

7. Switzerland

8. Belgium

9. A seasoned cheese sauce served over bread or toasted crackers . . . also called Welsh rarebit.

10. Melted, seasoned cheese into which cubes of bread are dipped and eaten with a long-handled fork. The classic fondue involves Swiss cheese seasoned with wine or kirsch . . . although "beef fondue" involves no cheese at all.

BIG BOOKS FOR

LITTLE EYEBALLS

Did they seem long because we were so short? Or because there was so much to them? No matter—here are some of the favorite big books of childhood. What memories—and "rememberies"—do they hold for you . . . ?

1. Who is Charles Dodgson?

2. Who wrote LITTLE WOMEN?

3. What was the name of Laura Ingalls Wilder's first LITTLE HOUSE book?

4. Name Johanna Spyri's story about a little Alpine lass.

5. What is the name of author P.L. Travers' magical nanny?

6. What is the name of L. Frank Baum's story about a little girl who is whisked away from Kansas by a cyclone and finds herself in a storybook land?

7. Beatrix Potter wrote and illustrated a whole series of animal stories, including "The Tale of Benjamin Bunny," but her most famous creation by far was ___________ ___________ ?

8. What is the name of the little boy in Rudyard Kipling's JUNGLE BOOKS who is raised by wolves?

9. What is the Newbery Medal?

10. What is the Caldecott Medal?

BIG BOOKS FOR LITTLE EYEBALLS

(Answers)

1. Charles Dodgson is the real name of Lewis Carroll, author of such favorites as ALICE'S ADVENTURES IN WONDERLAND and THROUGH THE LOOKING-GLASS.

2. Louisa May Alcott

3. LITTLE HOUSE IN THE BIG WOODS

4. HEIDI

5. Mary Poppins

6. THE WONDERFUL WIZARD OF OZ

7. Peter Rabbit

8. Mowgli

9. The annual award established by Frederic Melcher which goes to the best children's book of the previous year.

10. The annual award established by Frederic Melcher which goes to the most distinguished children's book illustrations of the previous year.

BUTCH AND SUNDANCE

From cattle-rustling to bank and train robbing, Butch and Sundance cut a wild trail across the face of the Old West. Some say they met their end in a hail of bullets in Bolivia. Others say they only made it look that way so they could change their ways and become honest men. You can believe what you want to, but either way you can be sure—they wouldn't want you to cheat on this Butch and Sundance Quiz.

1. Who was Robert LeRoy Parker?
2. Who was Harry Longabaugh?
3. What was the name of their gang?
4. Who was Etta Place?
5. Who played Butch in the 1969 movie BUTCH CASSIDY AND THE SUNDANCE KID?
6. Who played Sundance in the movie?
7. How did Butch get his nickname "Butch"?
8. Butch was born in April of 1866 on what unusual date?
9. What famous group of detectives pursued the gang across the U.S. and forced them to flee to South America?
10. What Earl Holliman TV show was *very* loosely based on the legend of the reformed Sundance Kid?

SUNDANCE FRIBBLE

Robert Redford hates cramped spaces, loves wide open spaces, and makes the most of the great outdoors on his sprawling Utah spread—*Sundance*.

BUTCH AND SUNDANCE

(Answers)

1. It was Butch Cassidy's given name.
2. It was the Sundance Kid's given name.
3. The Wild Bunch
4. Sundance's girlfriend
5. Paul Newman
6. Robert Redford
7. He used to be a butcher.
8. Friday the 13th
9. Pinkerton men
10. HOTEL DE PAREE

PARLEZ VOUS FOOD?

It's a small world, getting smaller each day—while our waistlines get bigger and bigger. What do you think? Are we eating our way to the center of the earth? When we get there, will it be chewy chocolate or mint that goes squirt?

One thing to remember—if we don't get there first, it may be called *centre de terre flambe!*

Just in case, you'd better brush up on your foreign food terminology. You never know . . . .

1. What's tempura?
2. What is meant by saute?
3. What's a croissant?
4. What's a la carte?
5. What is spaghetti al dente?
6. What is the literal meaning of hors d'oeuvres?
7. What's the literal meaning of shish kebab?
8. What is quiche?
9. What's another popular name for garbanzos?
10. What pasta gets its name from the Italian word for *tongue*?

PARLEZ VOUS FOOD?

(Answers)

1. It's a Japanese dish made of batter-dipped, deep-fried vegetables or seafoods . . . from the Japanese for *fried food.*
2. Sauteed food has been fried quickly in a small amount of fat . . . from the French word for *jumped.*
3. It's a light, buttery crescent roll . . . from the French word for *crescent.*
4. Selecting a meal a la carte means selecting each dish separately (and paying on a per-item basis) . . . from the French phrase for *according to the menu.*
5. Spaghetti al dente is not cooked until it is soft, but only until it can be chewed and offers some resistance when bitten . . . from the Italian for *to the teeth.*
6. Outside the works
7. Roast meat on a skewer . . . from the Turkish *shish* (skewer) and *kebap* (roast meat).
8. A pastry shell filled with an egg custard (often plus cheese, bacon, spinach, seafood, ad infinitum) and baked.
9. Chick peas
10. Linguini

THE MOVIES

The Man of Steel has scored great successes on TV, stage, radio, the printed page—and incidentally, in the movies. Maybe you've seen them all. If not, you've probably read about them, so here goes . . . .

1. Who was the screen's original Superman?
2. What was the first feature-length adventure of TV's Superman?
3. Who played Superman in #2?
4. Who played Lois Lane in #2?
5. The actress who played Lois Lane in the early serials and for a while on TV, but did not appear in #2, was __________ ?
6. In a brief scene in SUPERMAN: THE MOVIE, little Lois Lane is seen riding a train with her mom and pop. Who plays her parents?
7. Who plays Superman in SUPERMAN: THE MOVIE?
8. In #7, who plays Lois Lane?
9. In #7, who plays Perry White?
10. In #7, who plays Superman's Krypton father? His earth father?

SUPERMAN: THE MOVIES

(Answers)

1. Kirk Alyn
2. SUPERMAN AND THE MOLE MEN
3. George Reeves
4. Phyllis Coates
5. Noel Neill
6. Kirk Alyn and Noel Neill
7. Christopher Reeve
8. Margot Kidder
9. Jackie Cooper
10. Marlon Brando . . . Glenn Ford

ROMANTIC WASHINGTON

It's true! Hearts and flowers have a definite place in the Executive Mansion, where many a loving couple has tied the knot and even survived the pressures to live happily ever after . . . .

1. What First Couple gave birth to a future President?
2. Though James Buchanan is the only President never married, he was engaged. What happened to his fiancee?
3. Which First Couple celebrated their Silver Wedding Anniversary in the White House in 1877? In 1911?
4. What President married his ward in 1886?
5. Which President was married twice—the second time to his first wife's niece—then went on to have a daughter who was younger than his grandchildren?
6. Who was the only President to be married in the White House?
7. Who played matchmaker for Dolley and James Madison?
8. What former President gave his niece to FDR in marriage on St. Patrick's Day, 1905?
9. How are former Presidents Eisenhower and Nixon related by marriage?
10. Which President's last words were, "I love you, Sarah, for all eternity, I love you"?

ROMANTIC WASHINGTON

(Answers)

1. John Adams and Abigail Adams were the parents of John Quincy Adams.
2. She died of an overdose of laudanum when they had been engaged only a few months.
3. Rutherford and Lucy Hayes . . . William and Helen Taft
4. Grover Cleveland
5. Benjamin Harrison
6. Grover Cleveland
7. Aaron Burr
8. Theodore Roosevelt
9. Nixon's daughter Julie married Eisenhower's grandson David.
10. James K. Polk—and yes, Sarah was his wife.

BLUE AND GRAY

From 1861 to 1865, brother fought brother in the bloodiest war the United States had ever fought up to that time—and bloodier than any battle since for almost the next century, until World War II.

Although it's been more than 5 score and 15 years ago, it should take you considerably less than a century to supply these answers . . . .

1. Who was President of the U.S. when the Civil War began? When it ended?
2. What was Abraham Lincoln's middle name?
3. Who was the first President of the Confederacy?
4. How many states joined the Confederacy?
5. Name the Confederate states.
6. Where was the capital of the Confederacy?
7. Where was the first shot of the Civil War fired?
8. What was the first major battle of the Civil War?
9. What famous first involved the Monitor and the Merrimac? To which side did each belong?
10. What early machine gun—a sort of gigantic revolver with up to 10 rifle barrels—was first used in the Civil War?

BLUE AND GRAY

(Answers)

1. Abraham Lincoln . . . Abraham Lincoln
2. He didn't have one.
3. Jefferson Davis
4. Eleven
5. South Carolina, Alabama, Georgia, Florida, Louisiana, Mississippi, Texas (the original seven), Arkansas, Tennessee, Virginia and North Carolina
6. Richmond, Virginia
7. Fort Sumter
8. The Battle of Bull Run
9. It was the first action between ironclad ships. The Monitor belonged to the Union, the Merrimac to the Confederacy.
10. The Gatling Gun

AARFS ON THE AIRWAVES

Here are ten dogs you wouldn't mind inviting into your living room. They don't chew up shoes. They don't jump on delivery boys. And when you've had enough of them, you can always turn off your TV set.

But not just yet—at least, *don't touch that dial* until you've named these ten TV hounds.

1. The Douglas family's doggie on MY THREE SONS.
2. The ghost dog from TOPPER.
3. The real-live dog from THE GHOST AND MRS. MUIR.
4. Nick and Nora's sleuthful pup on THE THIN MAN.
5. The opinionated basset of PEOPLE'S CHOICE.
6. He does all kinds of good deeds, saves the day, and comes and goes like magic when people need a pal. He's ____________ ?
7. Corporal Rusty's best friend and a private in the U.S. Cavalry.
8. Jeff's collie, and later Timmy's. And before belonging to either of them, a movie star in her own right.
9. The bionic pooch of THE BIONIC WOMAN.
10. Uncle Bentley Gregg and niece Kelly's shaggy canine from BACHELOR FATHER.

AARFS ON THE AIRWAVES

(Answers)

1. Tramp
2. Neil
3. Scruffy
4. Asta
5. Cleo
6. Boomer
7. Rin-Tin-Tin
8. Lassie
9. Maximillian
10. Jasper

SEZ WHO TOO TOO

Welcome back to TV-land's horn of plenty—plenty of stars and the goodies they endorse. If you can match all their names with the products they promote, you've obviously been paying attention. Considering what the sponsors are paying for their services, that makes your attention one of the world's costliest commodities!

1. Ella Fitzgerald
2. Sylvester
3. Tony Randall
4. Popeye
5. Ken Berry
6. Tom Bosley
7. Jane Russell
8. Karl Malden
9. Candice Bergen
10. Meredith Baxter Birney

a. Dr. Pepper
b. Glad Trash Bags
c. Memorex
d. Playtex
e. Noxema
f. 9 Lives
g. Prima Salsa
h. Kinney Shoes
i. American Express
j. CIE

Answers:
1 *c*, 2 *f*, 3 *g*, 4 *a*, 5 *h*;
6 *b*, 7 *d*, 8 *i*, 9 *j*, 10 *e*

MR. MACHO

In a recent poll, the man who came out "Sexiest Male Celebrity in the World" was none other than this "Rough Cut" Romeo. By the way, Erik Estrada scored second, Clint Eastwood third—and if you score a perfect ten on this quiz, you've really got your Reynolds lore wrapped up!

1. Where was he born?
2. What was his nickname? Why?
3. In college he was an All-Southern Conference halfback headed for a pro football career. Why didn't he follow through?
4. He played Ben Frazer, Darren McGavin played Grey Holden, on the TV series ___________ ?
5. He played the blacksmith Quint Asper on TV's ___________ ?
6. He starred as a police detective in which two TV series?
7. What was his famous first for *Cosmopolitan* magazine?
8. He barely survives a canoe trip with Jon Voight in ___________ ?
9. Who was his co-star in THE MAN WHO LOVED CAT DANCING?
10. Before it belonged to Burt, who used Reynolds' home in Florida as a hideout from the law?

MR. MACHO

(Answers)

1. Waycross, Georgia

2. Buddy . . . to tell him apart from his father who was also named Burt.

3. He injured his knee in a game, then compounded the injury in an automobile accident.

4. RIVERBOAT

5. GUNSMOKE

6. DAN AUGUST and HAWK

7. He posed for its first male nude centerfold.

8. DELIVERANCE

9. Sarah Miles

10. Al Capone

SEZ WHO FROM THE WORLD OF SPORTS

Their pitches come straight from the world of sports into your own living room or den. And what are *you* doing? Taking it all in? Or doing a double-take when these eager, beaming faces pop up before your eyes selling—what? If you remember, this matching quiz should make you feel like a champ.

1. Joe DiMaggio
2. Fran Tarkenton
3. Nancy Lopez
4. Maury Wills and Sonny Jurgensen
5. Muhammad Ali
6. Tom Seaver
7. Don Meredith
8. Billie Jean King
9. Sugar Ray Leonard
10. Willie Mays and Mickey Mantle

a. Coke
b. Blue Bonnet
c. El Pro
d. Johnson's Baby Shampoo
e. Mr. Coffee
f. Light n' Lively
g. Nestea
h. d-Con
i. 7-UP
j. Lipton Tea

Answers:

1*e*, 2*d*, 3*a*, 4*c*, 5*h*,
6*f*, 7*i*, 8*g*, 9*j*, 10*b*

THE DUKE OF HOLLYWOOD

Hollywood's had its share of crown princes, a few contenders for the title "the King," any number of love gods, goddesses, and godlets—but there's only been one *Duke*. Not the Duke of Ellington. Not the Duke of Earl. But the Duke of Dukes, John Wayne . . .

1. What was John Wayne's given name?

2. Where was he born?

3. What character does he play in STAGECOACH, one of the milestone movies of his career?

4. Who is his co-star, the honky-tonk songstress Bijou, in SEVEN SINNERS?

5. In what movie does he construct a railroad bridge in the Andes and spend a night in Incan ruins?

6. Who plays Matt Garth in RED RIVER? Who plays Tom Dunson? How are the two related in the film?

7. In which movie does he play Sergeant John M. Stryker and help raise an American flag on Mt. Suribachi?

8. In THE QUIET MAN, why does he refuse to fight the town bully (his brother-in-law)? Who plays the bully? Who plays the quiet man's wife?

9. In which film does he play Temujin the Mongol? Who does he become by the end of the last reel?

10. Name the sequel to TRUE GRIT. Who co-stars?

THE DUKE OF HOLLYWOOD

(Answers)

1. Marion Michael Morrison
2. Winterset, Iowa
3. The Ringo Kid
4. Marlene Dietrich
5. TYCOON
6. Montgomery Clift . . . John Wayne . . . Matt is Tom's foster son.
7. SANDS OF IWO JIMA
8. Once, as a prize fighter, Sean Thornton (John Wayne) accidentally killed a man in the ring and no longer trusts his ability to control his strength. Victor McLaglen plays the bully and Maureen O'Hara plays Sean's wife.
9. THE CONQUEROR . . . Genghis Khan
10. ROOSTER COGBURN . . . Katharine Hepburn

WORSE THAN A CURSE

You may think there is nothing worse than a curse. But actually, there are several things. For instance, when a curse is fulfilled . . . or when your ole pal Don Elmo puts together a whole quiz about curses!

1. Vampires go West in this sinister Eric Fleming movie about a Dracula-like gunman.

2. In "The Rime of the Ancient Mariner," what bird does the sailor kill to deserve such rotten luck?

3. What playing card—for reasons buried in antiquity—is called "The Curse of Scotland"?

4. What Oliver Reed movie is about a young Spanish lad doomed to ghouldom by a family curse?

5. In what film does Margaret O'Brien portray a little Irish girl determined to lift a curse from three cantankerous men?

6. According to Oscar Wilde, work is the curse of whom?

7. Within a dozen years of the discovery of a famous Egyptian tomb, 21 people associated with it died, while others fell into bizarre circumstances. The year of the discovery was 1923. Who was buried in the tomb?

8. How many mummies come to life in the movie THE MUMMY'S CURSE?

9. Dana Andrews unearths an ancient stone and must "pass the parchment" or die in __________ ?

10. According to Tennyson, what is love's curse?

WORSE THAN A CURSE

(Answers)

1. CURSE OF THE UNDEAD
2. An Albatross
3. Nine of Diamonds
4. THE CURSE OF THE WEREWOLF
5. THREE WISE FOOLS
6. The drinking class
7. King Tutankhamun
8. Two
9. CURSE OF THE DEMON
10. Jealousy

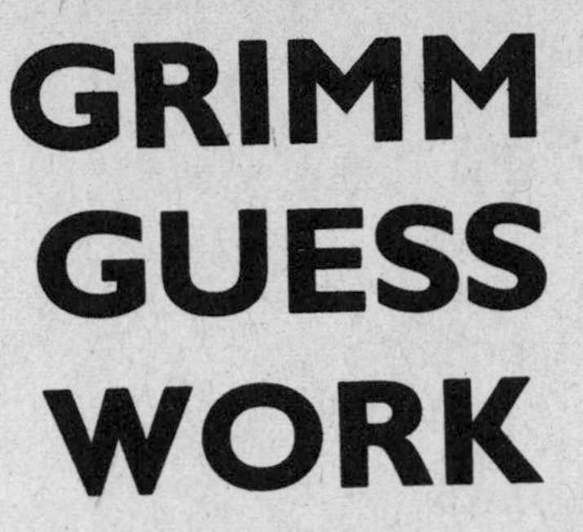

GRIMM GUESS WORK

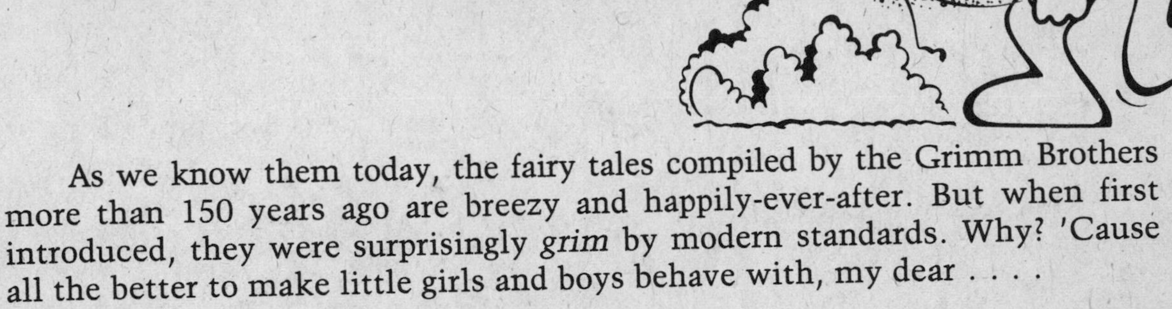

As we know them today, the fairy tales compiled by the Grimm Brothers more than 150 years ago are breezy and happily-ever-after. But when first introduced, they were surprisingly *grim* by modern standards. Why? 'Cause all the better to make little girls and boys behave with, my dear . . . .

1. When Red Riding Hood said to the wolf who was dressed as her grandmother, "What big teeth you have," what did he say?
2. What claim did the miller make about his daughter in RUMPELSTILTSKIN? What did the King say would happen to her if she couldn't make good on the promise?
3. Who pushed the witch into the oven, Hansel or Gretel?
4. Of what did the Brave Little Tailor kill "7 in one blow"?
5. What was Rapunzel's distinctive feature? What did the witch and the prince use it for?
6. What four kinds of animals were the Bremen Town Musicians?
7. By what name is Ashenputtel better known in the modern versions of her rags-to-riches story?
8. By what name is Briar Rose—who pricked her finger on her birthday and slept for a hundred years—better known?
9. What little fellow was so tiny he was fed to a cow and inadvertently swallowed by a wolf, then talked to the wolf from inside its stomach and tricked it into taking him home to his mother and father?
10. What are the names of the Grimm Brothers?

GRIMM GUESSWORK

(Answers)

1. "All the better to eat you with, my dear."
2. He said she could spin straw into gold . . . whereupon the King said that if she couldn't, she'd be put to death.
3. Gretel
4. Flies
5. Her very long hair . . . which the witch and the prince climbed up to get to her tower prison.
6. A donkey, a dog, a cat, and a rooster
7. Cinderella
8. Sleeping Beauty
9. Tom Thumb
10. Wilhelm and Jacob

MUPPET MAYHEM

Whether you know them from SESAME STREET, THE MUPPET SHOW, or THE MUPPET MOVIE—or even as personal friends—the point is, you *know* them or you've gone through the past decade with a bag over your head. So what if you have! Try your luck anyway on this Muppet quiz . . . .

1. Who is the creator of the Muppets?
2. Who is the puppeteer behind the Cookie Monster on SESAME STREET, Miss Piggy on THE MUPPET SHOW, and incidentally Yoda in STAR WARS: THE EMPIRE STRIKES BACK?
3. Who is known as "the Grouch"?
4. Who is the frog emcee of THE MUPPET SHOW?
5. What color is Big Bird?
6. What blue character goes by the description "lovable, furry, old ___________ "?
7. Who is the pink, pulchritudinous, porky femme fatale of THE MUPPET SHOW who considers her self-centeredness *entirely justified!*
8. Where can you find Milton Berle, Mel Brooks, Orson Welles, and Richard Pryor side-by-side with the Muppets on the same monster-size screen?
9. Which Muppet is spaced-out, wears dark glasses, and plays the saxophone?
10. On TV's THE MUPPET SHOW, how is Scooter related to the owner of the theater?

MUPPET MAYHEM

(Answers)

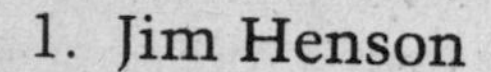

1. Jim Henson

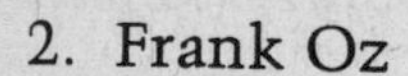

2. Frank Oz

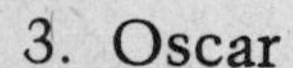

3. Oscar
4. Kermit

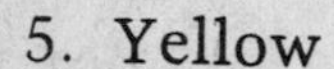

5. Yellow
6. Grover
7. Miss Piggy

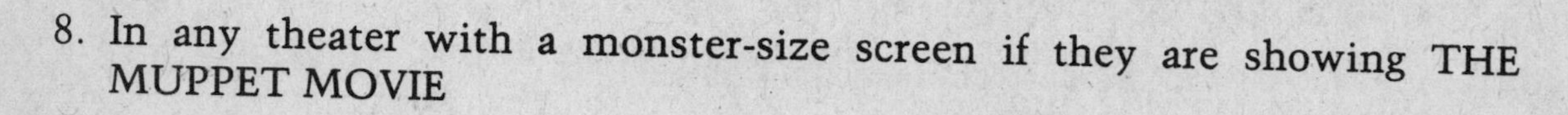

8. In any theater with a monster-size screen if they are showing THE MUPPET MOVIE

9. Zoot
10. Scooter is the owner's nephew.

TEN DESIRES

Flaming! Blazing! Beyond time! That's what the movie posters say about desire. Some people can take ten—count 'em, ten—desires, and have a very interesting agenda. Me, I take ten desires, and what do I have to show for them? A desire quiz! Maybe it's my mouthwash . . . .

1. Marlene Dietrich and Gary Cooper made a movie about a jewel thief (her) and a tourist (him). What was the movie?

2. What is the name of the Merle Oberon movie about a neurotic woman caught up in a whirlwind of yachting, drinking, and loving in Mexico?

3. Tab Hunter and Linda Darnell are marooned on a desert island, for all the good it does Tab, in __________ __________ __________ .

4. Name Tennessee Williams' play about Blanche DuBois and her in-laws, the Kowalskis.

5. Who was the woman in Napoleon's life whose name means "desired"?

6. Name the Eugene O'Neill play about a son who fixes his strict New England father's wagon by hitching up with his father's bride.

7. What is the Luis Bunuel film about a middle-aged man's unrequited love for a younger woman?

8. What Anthony Quinn film is actually a non-musical version of the opera CAVALLERIA RUSTICANA?

9. Greta Garbo has amnesia and returns to the husband she doesn't remember in __________ __________ __________ __________ .

10. Anne Baxter and Rock Hudson make smoldering love while Julie Adams goes up in smoke in __________ __________ .

TEN DESIRES

(Answers)

1. DESIRE
2. OF LOVE AND DESIRE
3. ISLAND OF DESIRE
4. A STREETCAR NAMED DESIRE
5. Desiree
6. DESIRE UNDER THE ELMS
7. THAT OBSCURE OBJECT OF DESIRE
8. FATAL DESIRE
9. AS YOU DESIRE ME
10. ONE DESIRE

THE MERSEY BEAT

During the period 1964-1968, mop-top English groups came on the scene with simple love lyrics and their own versions of the Beatles sound. How many of them can you remember?

1. These English groups that cropped up all during the Beatles period were said to have the "Mersey Beat." Why?

2. One group sang about Mrs. Brown's lovely daughter. The full name of the lead singer was Peter Blair Dennis Bernard Noone. What was his stage name and the name of the group?

3. "Glad All Over" was a big hit just when the Beatles were getting rolling. What fellow English band recorded it?

4. He comes from Scotland, sings about mellow yellow, sunshine supermen, and a girl called Lalena. He also married Brian Jones' ex-girlfriend. Who is he?

5. Which 60s group flapped their arms and legs up and down while singing "I'm Telling You Now"?

6. "Gimme Some Loving" and "I'm a Man" remind you of what group?

7. What group was composed of Billy Hinsche and two Hollywood scions of two superstar fathers?

8. Who were the two Hollywood lads of #7? Who were their fathers?

9. A small, frail blonde with a wispy voice made a hit of "As Tears Go By," written for her by her rock-and-roll boyfriend. Name her.

10. Name the rock-and-roll boyfriend mentioned in #9.

THE MERSEY BEAT

(Answers)

1. The Beatles and others were from Liverpool, England, and the Mersey is the river that runs through Liverpool.
2. Herman and the Hermits
3. The Dave Clark Five
4. Donovan Leitch . . . or simply "Donovan"
5. Freddie and the Dreamers
6. The Spencer Davis Group
7. Dino, Desi and Billy
8. Dino and Desi . . . Dino is the son of Dean Martin and Desi is the son of Desi Arnaz.
9. Marianne Faithfull
10. Mick Jagger

FUNNY MEN

This quiz could also be called "a fine mess" or "I'm a ba-a-a-ad boy," or "how sweet it is," but there's only one way to do justice to all these *funny men* at once. Come to think of it, this quiz doesn't do them nearly enough justice. So I guess the joke's on me!

1. Of the "fine mess" boys, Laurel and Hardy, which was the thin one and which was the fat one?

2. Which team made their unlikely movie debut in the Allan Jones musical ONE NIGHT IN THE TROPICS?

3. What TV funny man played a variety of TV characters that included Reggie Van Gleason, Poor Soul, and Ralph Kramden?

4. Who was TV's Clem Kadiddlehopper, Sheriff Deadeye, and The Mean Widdle Kid ("I dood it!")?

5. What now-famous—then not-so-famous—team of writers developed and wrote TV's GET SMART?

6. Who was the creator and sometimes director and writer of TV's THE DICK VAN DYKE SHOW? What role did he infrequently play on the show?

7. Who were Dorothy Lamour's two comic co-stars in the "ROAD" movies like ROAD TO MOROCCO and ROAD TO UTOPIA?

8. Who was the original host of TONIGHT (or THE TONIGHT SHOW)?

9. What TV gag-writer went on to star in BANANAS and ANNIE HALL?

10. Who cut LPs about his "button down mind," made movies like COLD TURKEY and HOT MILLIONS, and had two TV shows named after him?

FUNNY MEN

(Answers)

1. Stan Laurel was thin, Oliver Hardy was fat.
2. Bud Abbott and Lou Costello
3. Jackie Gleason
4. Red Skelton
5. Mel Brooks and Buck Henry
6. Carl Reiner . . . Alan Brady
7. Bing Crosby and Bob Hope
8. Steve Allen
9. Woody Allen
10. Bob Newhart

BEHIND EVERY SUCCESSFUL PUPPET

They say a puppeteer is really successful when people begin to forget his or her connection with the puppet. For instance, W.C. Fields used to get so enraged at the smart-mouth Charlie McCarthy he'd forget Charlie was made of wood . . . but he'd never raise his voice at Edgar Bergen.

Would you know who to blow your stack at if you had a quarrel with one of these famous puppets? If not, the names of their other selves are on the next page.

1. Hush Puppy
2. Farfel
3. Ollie Dragon
4. Jerry Mahoney
5. Mortimer Snerd
6. Madam
7. The Muppets
8. Snarky Parker
9. Judy Splinters
10. "'S all right"

BEHIND EVERY SUCCESSFUL PUPPET

(Answers)

1. Shari Lewis
2. Jimmy Nelson
3. Burr Tillstrom
4. Paul Winchell
5. Edgar Bergen
6. Wayland Flowers
7. Jim Henson
8. Bil & Cora Baird
9. Shirley Dinsdale
10. Senor Wences

BETTER MOUSETRAPS

Just imagine—you're all alone in your house and the whole world is outside, pushing against the windows. If that doesn't appeal to you, don't be an inventor, because you know what they say about building a better mousetrap. Just ask any of these guys, or at least match them with their inventions . . .

1. Sewing machine	a. Cyrus W. Field
2. Cotton gin	b. Chester Carlson
3. Transatlantic cable	c. Alexander Graham Bell
4. Typewriter	d. Elias Howe
5. Telephone	e. Wallace H. Carothers
6. X Ray	f. Eli Whitney
7. Wireless telegraphy	g. Ferdinand von Zeppelin
8. Dirigible	h. Christopher Sholes
9. Xerox	i. Guglielmo Marconi
10. Nylon	j. Wilhelm von Roentgen

Answers:

1*d*, 2*f*, 3*a*, 4*h*, 5*c*,
6*j*, 7*i*, 8*g*, 9*b*, 10*e*.

YOU MUST REMEMBER THIS

Movies may come and go but there's only one CASABLANCA. As popular as it was when it first came out, it's become a thousand times more popular since then. No true trivia fanatic has seen it fewer than 10 times. How about you?

1. What is the name of Rick's cafe?
2. What does he have that Laszlo wants?
3. Who did Rick get them from?
4. Who plays Renault?
5. Why does Renault close down the cafe? What excuse does he give?
6. Who's the piano player?
7. What song did Rick tell him not to play?
8. Who does he play it for in spite of Rick's orders?
9. Where do Signor Ferrari and Rick discuss the news about Ugarte?
10. Who shoots Major Strasser? Who covers for him?

YOU MUST REMEMBER THIS

(Answers)

1. Rick's Cafe Americain

2. Letters of transit that cannot be rescinded or even questioned.

3. Ugarte (Peter Lorre)

4. Claude Rains

5. Strasser demands that Renault close it because the honor of the Reich has been insulted with the singing of the French "Marseillaise." The excuse Renault gives is that gambling has been going on in a back room. (He gives the excuse while pocketing his winnings).

6. Sam (Dooley Wilson)

7. "As Time Goes By"

8. Ilsa Laszlo (Ingrid Bergman)

9. The Blue Parrot

10. Rick . . . Renault

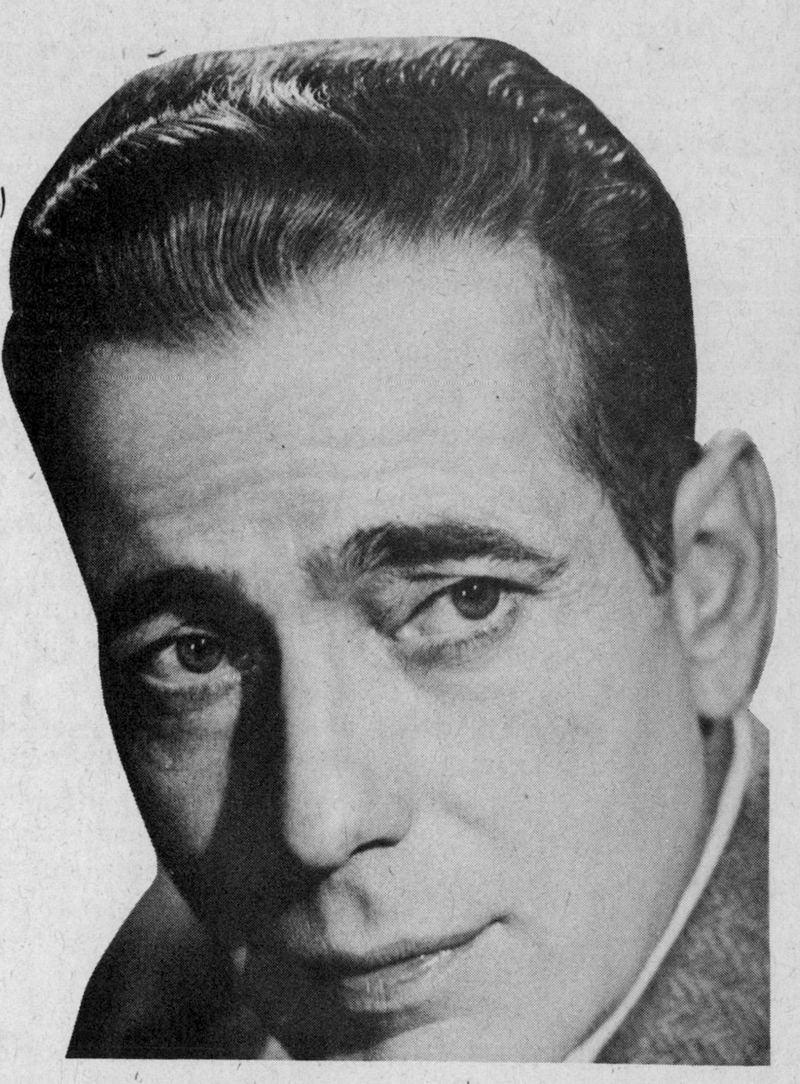

FEMMES FATALES

All things considered, it's only fair that we take a stroll through this female rogues gallery. After all, we can't have a quiz on He-nanigans and let the ladies get off scott-free!

1. According to Biblical history, who robs Samson of his strength by cutting his hair?

2. In what movie does Mae West sing an operatic—yes, *operatic!*—portrayal of #1?

3. What temptress does legend tell us turned Ulysses' men into swine?

4. In a sort of reversal of #3, who appears to be running for President on the August 1980 cover of *Life* magazine? (Hint: She's surrounded by dozens of bug-eyed frogs).

5. In what movie of the Old South does Bette Davis create a scandal by wearing a daring red gown to a society ball?

6. Who was the silver screen's first vamp? (Hint: Her name is an anagram for *Arab Death*).

7. By what name was Margaretha Geertruide Zelle MacLeod, notorious enchantress and World War I spy, better known?

8. What female partner of a husband-and-wife team regularly appeared in musical "v-a-m-p, vamp" segments of their popular TV variety show?

9. Who goes by the name of "Lust" in the movie BEDAZZLED?

10. Who plays the love goddess statue come to life in the movie ONE TOUCH OF VENUS? Who created the role on Broadway?

FEMMES FATALES

(Answers)

1. Delilah
2. GOIN' TO TOWN
3. Circe
4. Miss Piggy
5. JEZEBEL
6. Theda Bara
7. Mata Hari
8. Cher
9. Raquel Welch
10. Ava Gardner . . . Mary Martin

HEAVENS ABOVE

Once mankind discovered the earth was round, it became perfectly clear that the heavens were not only above but encircling and even below us. People who didn't want to drop off into the deep, dark depths of the solar system were not amused. Too bad for them. Think how it might have improved their scores on this cosmic quiz . . . .

1. What is the difference between the cosmos and a solar system?
2. Name the planets of our solar system.
3. Why is it called our *solar* system?
4. Which is the only planet discovered in the 20th century?
5. Which is the largest planet?

6. Which of the planets is closest to Earth?
7. Which planet has the most moons?
8. Which is called "the angry red planet"?
9. America's Pilgrim 10 and Pilgrim 11, and Travelers 1 and 2 space probes, reported back vital data concerning Neptune and Uranus in the late 1970s—True or False?
10. Which planet has long been known for its ring? Around which other planet did astronauts first see a ring in 1977?

HEAVENS ABOVE

(Answers)

1. The cosmos is the entire universe . . . a solar system is only one star plus its planets and their moons, along with asteroids, planetoids, comets, and other celestial matter.

2. Mercury, Venus, Earth, Mars, Jupiter, Saturn, Uranus, Neptune, Pluto

3. *Solar* refers to our sun around which this system of planets and astral bodies revolves.

4. Pluto

5. Jupiter

6. Venus

7. Jupiter . . . with at least 13 and possibly 14.

8. Mars

9. False . . . however America's Pioneers 10 and 11 and Voyagers 1 and 2 did report back on Jupiter in the mid and late 1970s.

10. Saturn . . . Uranus

BASEBALL BACK WHEN

Would you be able to trace baseball's origins back to the old colonial game of one old cat? Or town ball? Relax—neither could I without looking it up. But these questions about baseball history *aren't* that hard, so you'll have no excuse whatever for striking out!

1. Who first named the game "baseball"?

2. Where did Abner Doubleday lay out his first baseball diamond? What famous institution is there now?

3. Which was organized first, the National League or the American League?

4. What was the name of the first all-professional team, formed in 1869?

5. What popular mixed-bag event was first organized by Arch Ward, sports editor of the *Chicago Tribune*, in 1933?

6. Eight players were accused of plotting to throw the 1919 World Series to Cincinnati in return for a substantial payoff. To what team did they belong? By what name is the scandal known?

7. Who retired in 1950 after an almost unbelievable 50 years as manager of the Philadelphia Athletics?

8. Which team became the first to win five successive pennants? Who was their manager?

9. What historic World Series "first" occurred on October 8, 1956?

10. Who was the first player elected to the National Baseball Hall of Fame?

BASEBALL BACK WHEN

(Answers)

1. Abner Doubleday

2. Cooperstown, New York . . . The Baseball Museum and Hall of Fame

3. The National League (1876) . . . The American League was not formed until 1900.

4. The Cincinnati Red Stockings

5. The All-Star Game

6. The Chicago White Sox . . . "The Black Sox Scandal"

7. Connie Mack

8. The New York Yankees . . . Casey Stengel

9. The first perfect no-hit, no-run game in World Series history, pitched by Yankee Don Larsen against the Brooklyn Dodgers.

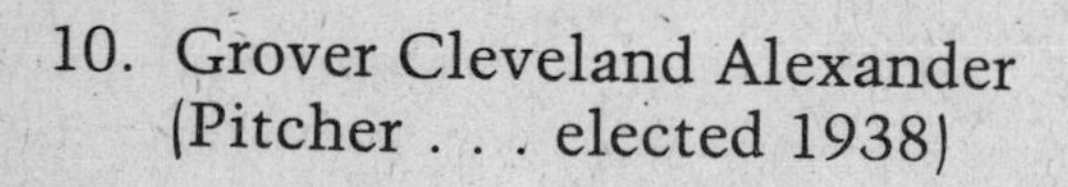

10. Grover Cleveland Alexander (Pitcher . . . elected 1938)

FRIBB-BALL

Recent studies show that major league baseball players average longer lifespans than the rest of the male populace, with third basemen living longest of all.

THE BIGGER THEY ARE . . .

. . . the harder they are to forget, which is why you should feel like a mental giant as you whip through this assortment of the largest, tallest, and biggest attractions . . . .

1. What's the world's largest unbroken political unit—occupying more than one seventh of the land area of the globe?

2. What is the world's largest island?

3. What is the world's highest mountain peak and where is it located?

4. What is the world's largest ocean?

5. What is the world's longest river?

6. What is the name and location of the world's highest waterfall?

7. What and where is the world's highest desert?

8. What and where is the highest mountain in the U.S.?

9. What and where is the deepest U.S. lake?

10. What and where is the largest inland bay in the U.S.?

THE BIGGER THEY ARE . . .

(Answers)

1. The Soviet Union
2. Greenland
3. Everest . . . in the Himalayan range between Nepal and Tibet.
4. The Pacific Ocean
5. The Nile
6. Angel Falls in Venezuela
7. Atacama . . . located in Northern Chile
8. Mount McKinley . . . Alaska
9. Crater Lake . . . Oregon
10. The Chesapeake Bay . . . which divides Maryland into an Eastern and Western shore and extends well into Virginia.

DISCO FILE

It started in France, came to New York, then swept the world to become a way of life. Disco dancing took up where big band dancing left off and huge halls once again filled with swaying, gyrating bodies. If you're still not sure what they were doing, this quiz might give you a few clues . . . .

1. What dance kicked the disco craze off to a flying start?

2. Disco is said to be influenced by a Spanish beat first popularized by the kids of New York's El Barrio. What is the beat called?

3. Two of the very first disco hits were by Gloria Gaynor and Barry White. What was hers? What was his?

4. For a while, one new record label seemed to have a monopoly on disco music. What label?

5. The man who founded #4 is also credited with the discovery of Donna Summer, The Village People, and others. What's his name?

6. Long about 1973, The Hues Corporation came up with a phenomenal hit single. What was it called?

7. What controversial New York disco became famous for its policy of admitting only jet-setters and people whose flaky attire got them through the door?

8. "The ultimate disco movie" stars Valerie Perrine, ex-Olympian Bruce Jenner, and a well-known disco group. What is the movie?

9. What is the group featured in #8?

10. When the Walt Disney people came out with a disco record, Donald Duck performed one of its songs on the TV commercials. Which song?

DISCO FILE

(Answers)

1. The Hustle
2. Salsa
3. "Never Can Say Goodbye" . . . "Can't Get Enough of Your Love, Babe"
4. Casablanca Records
5. Neil Bogart
6. "Rock The Boat"
7. Studio 54
8. CAN'T STOP THE MUSIC
9. The Village People
10. "Macho Duck"

BIJOU-BALL

No, it's not a new kind of ball game. It's a quiz about those flicks on sportsfolk and those sportsfolk in flicks that have appeared at your local Bijou, Loews, or neighborhood movie house!

1. Who plays Jimmy Piersall in FEAR STRIKES OUT?

2. Who plays golfer Ben Hogan in FOLLOW THE SUN?

3. Where does Bob Hope, as New York Mayor James Walker, resign from office in the movie BEAU JAMES?

4. What World Figure Skating Champion plays Snow White in SNOW WHITE AND THE THREE STOOGES?

5. Another skating star appears in SUN VALLEY SERENADE, EVERYTHING HAPPENS AT NIGHT, and THIN ICE. Who is she?

6. What Olympic swimming champ has played Tarzan in more movies than anyone else?

7. Another Olympic swimming star has portrayed Flash Gordon, Buck Rogers, and occasionally Tarzan. Who?

8. What early sports great does Ronald Reagan portray in THE WINNING TEAM?

9. What is Gary Cooper's role in THE PRIDE OF THE YANKEES?

10. What former gridiron All-American All-Pro stars opposite Raquel Welch in 100 RIFLES?

BIJOU-BALL

(Answers)

1. Anthony Perkins
2. Glenn Ford
3. Yankee Stadium
4. Carol Heiss
5. Sonja Henie
6. Johnny Weissmuller
7. Buster Crabbe
8. Grover Cleveland Alexander
9. Lou Gehrig
10. Jim Brown

A BABE FRIBBLE

What the sportsworld won't do for showbusiness! When Harry Frazee was owner of the Boston Red Sox, he sold the Babe to the New York Yankees to raise production funds for the musical comedy NO, NO NANETTE. At least NANETTE was a smash hit—twice!

SPORTS STARS—MALE

These names from some of America's favorite sports are sure to be familiar—but let's see how good you are at remembering the details of the careers that go with them!

1. What golf great was a 40s champ, suffered a debilitating auto wreck, then returned to win both the U.S. Open and the Masters in the early 50s?

2. Who stands 7′ 2″, has an IQ of 131, and signed with the Milwaukee Bucks for a million-and-a-half dollars when he finished college?

3. What Englishman is considered by many to be the greatest racing driver ever, winning 194 of his 466 races—a record no other driver even approaches?

4. Who was the second man in history to win tennis' Grand Slam—Wimbledon, Australia, France, U.S.A.—in one year?

5. What American Indian track star was voted by sportswriters "the greatest all-round athlete of the last half century"?

6. Who, according to the Baseball Hall of Fame, was the "greatest drawing card in the history of baseball"?

7. Who won the last bare-knuckle prizefight in history?

8. Whose autobiography is subtitled "Just Like Any Other 7-Foot Black Millionaire Who Lives Next Door"?

9. When professional baseball celebrated its 100th anniversary in 1969 by naming its greats, who was voted Greatest Living Player?

10. What New York Jets quarterback predicted his team would win the 1969 Super Bowl and turned out to be absolutely right?

SPORTS STARS—MALE

(Answers)

1. Ben Hogan
2. Kareem Abdul-Jabbar
3. Stirling Moss
4. Rod Laver
5. Jim Thorpe
6. Babe Ruth
7. John L. Sullivan
8. Wilt Chamberlain's
9. Joe DiMaggio
10. Joe Namath

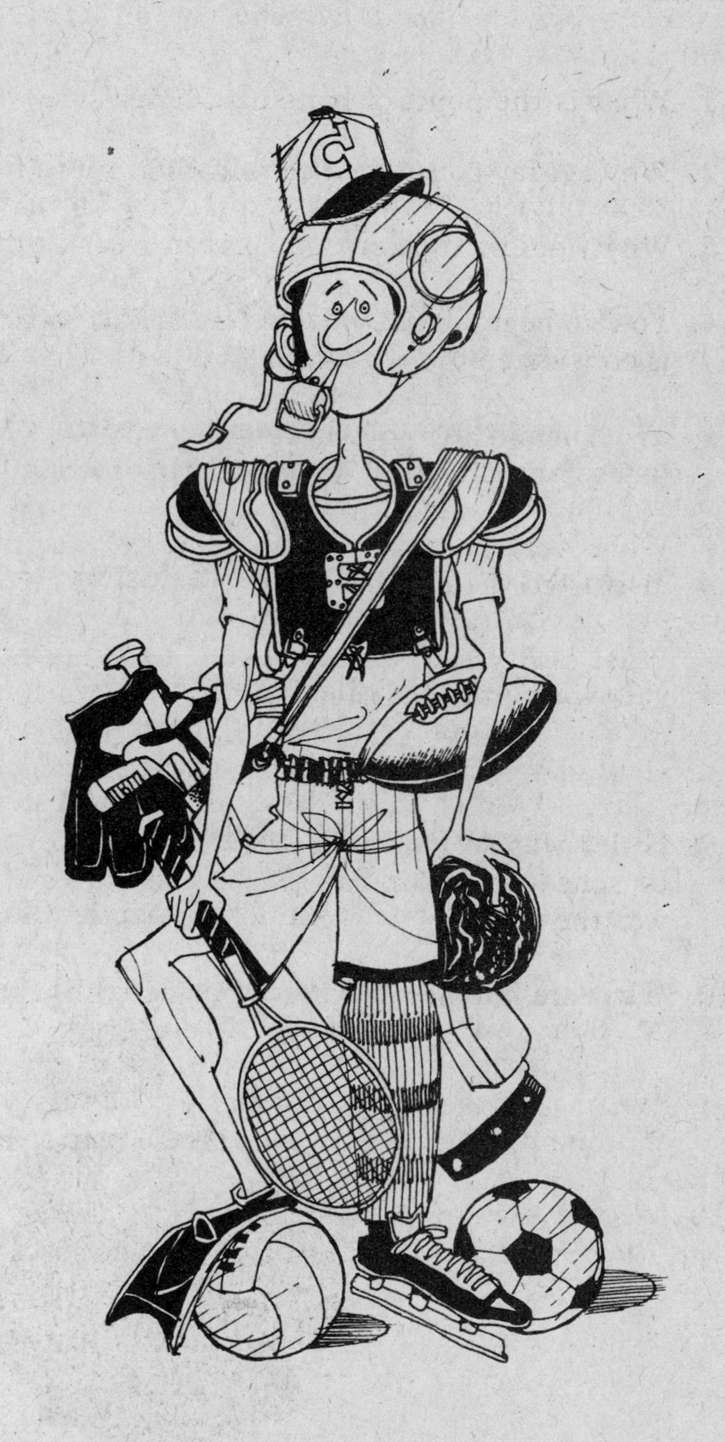

EVIL EYE ETIQUETTE

Maybe you're one of those people who thinks it's fun pretending you aren't superstitious . . . or one of those others who gets your kicks pretending you are. Either way, we'll find out soon enough. Unless you're planning to dismiss a perfect score as *mere coincidence* . . . .

1. What is the point of hanging a horseshoe with the legs pointed upward?
2. Why is May considered an unlucky month for getting married?
3. Why would a superstitious person wear clothing inside-out?
4. You've heard about getting out of the "wrong side" of bed? Which side is considered the wrong side?
5. In Leonardo da Vinci's famous painting "The Last Supper," what has Judas done that a superstitious person would immediately correct?
6. What very famous French general was morbidly afraid of cats and distrusted the number 13?
7. What is Eve said to have taken with her from the Garden of Eden that is now a symbol of good luck?
8. How many years of bad luck go with breaking a mirror?
9. Hitler was so fond of a particular number that he went out of his way to schedule major battles on the corresponding calendar dates. What was the number?
10. What are bubbles in coffee considered likely to indicate? Bubbles in tea?

EVIL EYE ETIQUETTE

(Answers)

1. If the legs point downward, the good luck will run out.
2. The ancient Romans honored their dead in May.
3. If you wear your clothing inside-out, the Devil is less likely to recognize you.
4. The left side is the wrong side. The idea is to get out of bed on the right side, starting with your right foot first.
5. He has spilled salt. (He is also the 13th person at the table).
6. Napoleon Bonaparte
7. A four-leaf clover
8. Seven
9. Seven
10. Money . . . visitors

THE QUEEN OF DISCO

This quiz is about—who else—Donna Summer. Ever since her smash recording of "Love To Love You Baby," her voice and sound have almost monopolized dance floor charts. Add to her vocal range that great beauty and stage presence—no wonder she's one of the brightest stars of the disco heavens!

1. Who produced her first hit single and was responsible for the overall production of her subsequent sound?
2. In which city of the world was American-born Donna discovered?
3. What is her real name? Where does "Summer" come from?
4. Which disco-oriented film does she star in?
5. How long was the original recording of the controversial "Love To Love You, Baby"?
6. What is the name of her greatest hits collection?
7. Which song won her a Grammy Award for Best Female Vocal?
8. Who sings with her on her hit "Heaven Knows"?
9. What is her daughter's name?
10. What song, made famous by Richard Harris in the 60s and written by Jim Webb, did Donna re-record as a disco number?

THE QUEEN OF DISCO

(Answers)

1. Giorgio Moroder and Pete Bellotte
2. In Munich, Germany, where she was doing studio work
3. Donna Gaines . . . Her ex-husband's name was Helmut Sommer, which she Americanized by making it "Summer."
4. TGIF
5. 16 minutes, 50 seconds
6. "On The Radio," Parts I & II
7. "Last Dance"
8. Joe Esposito
9. Mimi
10. "MacArthur Park"

FUNNY LADIES

Once it was forbidden for women to appear to be funny in public. The result, I suppose, was that people were forever laughing at men until men got a complex and decided to allow women to be funny too. This gave rise to comediennes and at least one comediennes trivia quiz . . . .

1. The musicals FUNNY GIRL and FUNNY LADY are based on the life of what legendary comedienne?
2. Which of these Lucille Ball movies also stars Desi Arnaz—THE LONG, LONG TRAILER . . . FOLLOW THE FLEET . . . MAME?
3. Who plays Ma Kettle to Percy Kilbride's Pa Kettle in more than a half-dozen flicks of the late 40s and 50s?
4. What slapstick comedienne and remarkable jazz singer was born Margaret Theresa Yvonne Reed?
5. Who played Joan in TV's classic sitcom I MARRIED JOAN?
6. Diana Canova's mother was one of the big hits of the Ziegfeld Follies and movies like CAROLINA CANNONBALL. What was her name?
7. Her first comedy LP was "Wet Toe In A Hot Socket" and she's been called the "female Bob Hope." Who is *she*?
8. Who was Mike Nichols' long-time comedy partner as well as Walter Matthau's co-star in A NEW LEAF?
9. Who played Mrs. Hickenlooper to Sid Caesar's Mr. Hickenlooper on YOUR SHOW OF SHOWS?
10. Who was the first Trixie Norton on CBS's THE HONEYMOONERS?

FUNNY LADIES

(Answers)

1. Fanny Brice
2. THE LONG, LONG TRAILER
3. Marjorie Main
4. Martha Raye
5. Joan Davis
6. Judy Canova
7. Phyllis Diller
8. Elaine May
9. Imogene Coca
10. Joyce Randolph

BETRAYED!

Whoever first said "all's fair in love and war" was laying out the age-old ground rules for betrayal and treason. This is not to say that other things don't lead to betrayal. It's just that you have to look harder to find them!

1. What American patriot said "If this be treason, make the most of it!"?
2. When this man betrayed Norway to the Nazis, his name became synonymous with the word *traitor*. What was his name?
3. In what classic film does Victor McLaglen betray his friends for a handful of money during the Irish Rebellion?
4. In what film does John Wayne, as Lynn Hollister, investigate a murder at the Club Inferno?
5. What American patriot, when hanged for treason by the British, said, "I only regret that I have but one life to lose for my country!"?
6. Name the movie in which William Holden, as a double agent, falls in love with Lilli Palmer, who is executed for helping him.
7. Of the men who assassinated Julius Caesar, only one—his dear friend—caused him to cry out, "And *you*?" Name the friend.
8. In fact, Caesar had a lot of trouble with friends betraying him. Which of his friends took up with Cleopatra after Caesar married her?
9. In what battle did another Caesar defeat Cleopatra and this turncoat?
10. Name the American who was discovered in a plot to betray West Point to the British during the Revolutionary War.

BETRAYED!

(Answers)

1. Patrick Henry
2. Vidkun *Quisling*
3. THE INFORMER
4. A MAN BETRAYED
5. Nathan Hale
6. THE COUNTERFEIT TRAITOR
7. Brutus . . . as in *et tu, Brute!*
8. Mark Antony
9. In the very decisive battle of Actium (31 B.C.), the future Augustus Caesar defeated Mark Antony when Cleopatra's ships deserted Mark's and fled.
10. Benedict Arnold

SPORTS STARS—FEMALE

Here's a jumble of famous ladies from the sports world. If you can't do as well on the highlights of their careers as you did on SPORTS STARS—MALE, you may have to answer to the ERA!

1. What all-round female great triumphed over cancer to win the women's national open in 1954?
2. Who defeated Bobby Riggs in the headline-making Battle of the Sexes tennis showdown of 1973?
3. Who was first to win the Olympic Figure Skating Women's Singles three years in a row . . . 1928, 1932, and 1936?
4. Who was the first woman in tennis to score a Grand Slam and how old was she at the time?
5. Who was the first woman to swim the English Channel in *both* directions?
6. Who became, in 1957, the first black to win the U.S. national singles championship and incidentally, the Wimbledon women's singles crown in the same year?
7. In which sport did Australian Dawn Fraser become one of the all-time greats?
8. What figure skater won the U.S.'s only gold medal in the 1968 Olympics in Grenoble, France?
9. Who became, in 1971, the first woman athlete in history to earn over $100,000 in a single year?
10. Who won the world cycling championships in 1973 and 1976 and became, also in 1976, the first person to win three Olympic medals—gold, silver, and bronze—in speed skating?

SPORTS STARS—FEMALE

(Answers)

1. Mildred ''Babe'' Didrikson Zaharias
2. Billie Jean King
3. Sonja Henie
4. Maureen (''Little Mo'') Connolly . . . 18
5. Florence Chadwick
6. Althea Gibson
7. Swimming
8. Peggy Fleming
9. Billie Jean King
10. Sheila Young

PERENNIAL CO-STARS

Nothing beats a winning combination—which is why the same stars can be paired over and over again, until they get sick of it or each other or worse, we do. Yet here are ten teams always worth watching. Can you identify them from the movies they made together?

1. FLYING DOWN TO RIO, SWING TIME, TOP HAT?
2. DESK SET, ADAM'S RIB, WITHOUT LOVE?
3. A SONG IS BORN, WONDER MAN, THE SECRET LIFE OF WALTER MITTY?
4. KEY LARGO, THE BIG SLEEP, TO HAVE AND HAVE NOT?
5. PENNY SERENADE, THE AWFUL TRUTH, MY FAVORITE WIFE?
6. THE ADVENTURES OF ROBIN HOOD, THEY DIED WITH THEIR BOOTS ON, SANTA FE TRAIL?
7. SEVENTH HEAVEN, SUNNY SIDE UP, HIGH SOCIETY BLUES?
8. THE GIRL OF THE GOLDEN WEST, BITTER SWEET, I MARRIED AN ANGEL?
9. THE SANDPIPER, WHO'S AFRAID OF VIRGINIA WOOLF, THE TAMING OF THE SHREW?
10. THE MASK OF DIMITRIOS. THREE STRANGERS, THE VERDICT?

PERENNIAL CO-STARS

(Answers)

1. Fred Astaire and Ginger Rogers
2. Katharine Hepburn and Spencer Tracy
3. Virginia Mayo and Danny Kaye
4. Humphrey Bogart and Lauren Bacall
5. Irene Dunne and Cary Grant

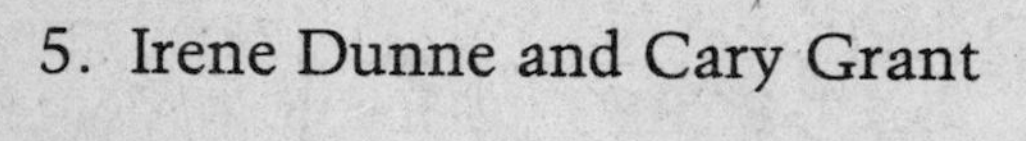

6. Olivia de Havilland and Erroll Flynn
7. Janet Gaynor and Charles Farrell
8. Jeanette MacDonald and Nelson Eddy
9. Richard Burton and Elizabeth Taylor
10. Peter Lorre and Sydney Greenstreet

FAIRWAY FACTS

If you whack a little white ball across a net, it's called tennis. If you whack an even littler one across the ground with a stick, it's called golf. Of course, there are other differences between the two games, and if you don't know them, maybe you'd better chalk this off as a hazard or trap and go on to the next quiz . . . .

1. How many holes must you play to play a round of golf?

2. Scoring one stroke under par on a hole is called a __________ ?

3. Scoring two strokes under par, except on a par-3 hole, is called a __________ ?

4. Scoring two strokes under par on a par-3 hole is a __________ ?

5. Scoring one stroke over par on a hole is a __________ ?

6. The chunk of turf that often accompanies a golf ball when it leaves the ground is called a __________ ?

7. The championship played annually at Augusta National Golf Club, in Georgia, which Arnold Palmer has won four times, is called the __________ .

8. What is the oldest international amateur golf team match and which two countries are represented?

9. Where was the first 18-hole course in the United States?

10. Mary, Queen of Scots, may have been the first female golfer. The people who carried her clubs were called pupils or *cadets*. Now, what do you suppose that word became in modern golf?

FAIRWAY FACTS

(Answers)

1. 18
2. Birdie
3. Eagle
4. Hole-in-one
5. Bogey
6. Divot
7. Masters
8. Walker Cup . . . the United States and Great Britain
9. Wheaton, Illinois (opened in 1893)
10. Caddies

A GOLF FRIBBLE

The 13th hole in the 1938 PGA tournament was unlucky for Jimmy Hines, lucky for Sam Snead—when Hines's shot sent both balls into the cup. Final score? Snead won by one stroke.

FIDO AND FRIENDS

Ever since the dawn of time when they became the first animals tamed by people, dogs have been surprisingly loyal to the human race. You might think this indicates a lack of intelligence, but it doesn't! They're among the top-rated on that score in the animal kingdom. And speaking of scores, you'd better get at least seven out of ten on these questions, or you can head straight for the doghouse!

1. What breed of dog is TV and Hollywood's Lassie?
2. What breed is Rin-Tin-Tin?
3. What African hound is the only breed of dog that can't bark?
4. What are the largest dogs? The smallest?
5. What is the A.K.C.?
6. How many breeds does the A.K.C. recognize as purebreds?
7. Which of these is not a breed of dog—kelpie, cerberus, borzoi?
8. Why does a dog stick out its tongue and pant when it becomes overheated or excited?
9. What is the name of the fox terrier who accompanied Admiral Richard Byrd to the North and South poles?
10. What is the name of the world's first space-animal—the dog sent into space by the Russians in 1957?

FIDO AND FRIENDS

(Answers)

1. Collie

2. German Shepherd

3. Basenji

4. Irish wolfhounds . . . chihuahuas

5. American Kennel Club, the chief organization of dog breeders in the U.S.

6. 112

7. Cerberus . . . which was the name of the three-headed dog in Greek mythology whose job it was to guard the gates of the underworld.

8. It's a cooling process, dogs being short-changed on sweat glands, which they only have in their feet and on their noses.

9. Igloo

10. Laika

HITHER AND YON

They say travel is broadening—and if you eat along the way, it certainly can be—so if you'd like to spare yourself the calories and a few thousand dollars, how about a little arm-chair visit to the four corners of the earth? You can prove yourself a globe-trotter-plus by naming the cities and countries that boast these spectacular sights.

1. Taj Mahal
2. Red Square
3. Champs-Elysees
4. Ginza
5. Rijksmuseum
6. Parthenon
7. St. Mark's Square
8. Westminster Abbey
9. Prado
10. Tivoli Gardens

Question: What's this?

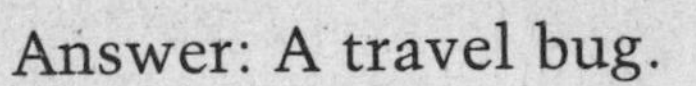

Answer: A travel bug.

HITHER AND YON

(Answers)

1. Agra, India
2. Moscow, U.S.S.R.
3. Paris, France
4. Tokyo, Japan
5. Amsterdam, The Netherlands (Holland)
6. Athens, Greece
7. Venice, Italy
8. London, England
9. Madrid, Spain
10. Copenhagen, Denmark

CELEBRITY STAR-SIGNS

Can the Zodiac reveal someone's secret self, or help determine a personality? Who can say for sure . . . ? But if you're up to making a few educated guesses, here are ten famous names.

See if you can guess their signs . . . .

1. Ed Asner
2. Barbra Streisand
3. Sophia Loren
4. Laurence Olivier
5. Neil Simon
6. Woody Allen
7. Thomas Edison
8. Howard Cosell
9. Victor Mature
10. Marcello Mastroianni

CELEBRITY STAR-SIGNS

(Answers)

1. Scorpio ("the qualities that soldiers are made of")
2. Taurus ("appreciation of the basics—eating, drinking, loving")
3. Virgo ("practical mentality, capable of great love")
4. Gemini ("intellectual, ambitious, sensitive")
5. Cancer ("does best with a woman who gives emotional support")
6. Sagittarius ("highly intellectual, farseeing, imaginative")
7. Aquarius ("progressive, sometimes unorthodox and shocking")
8. Aries ("plunges ahead without fear or favor")
9. Capricorn ("driven by security and power needs")
10. Libra ("expert in all matters pertaining to love")

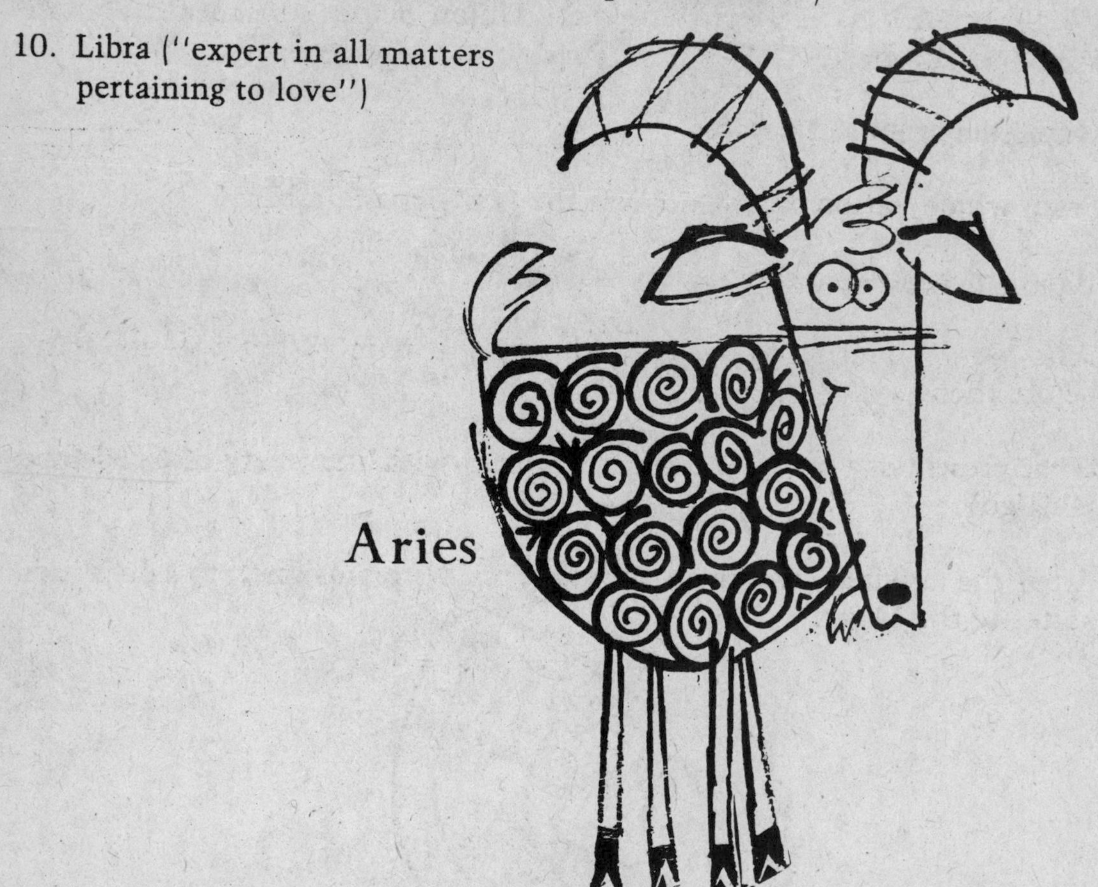

Aries

THE GROWTH OF A NATION

Population-wise, the U.S. gets bigger every day. Land-wise, some coastal regions are continually eroding into the ocean.

Never fear. When the U.S. has washed away down to the size of a hatbox, we'll stand our entire population vertically and reach to Mars.

Economically—at last!

Until then, you'll have to satisfy yourself with knowing when each of these areas joined the U.S. of A.

1. When did Hawaii become a state?
2. When did Alaska become a state?
3. Before Alaska became a state, which was the largest state in the Union?
4. What was the last state to enter the Union before Alaska and Hawaii? Who was President?
5. Name the original 13 states.
6. From which nation did we acquire the Louisiana Purchase?
7. What states did the Louisiana Purchase become?
8. Who was President when Texas became a state? What was its status before then?
9. What present-day states were first acquired with the treaty of Guadelupe-Hidalgo?
10. After the original 13 states, which President was first to admit new states to the Union?

THE GROWTH OF A NATION

(Answers)

1. August 21, 1959
2. January 3, 1959
3. Texas
4. Arizona . . . William Howard Taft
5. Massachusetts, Rhode Island, Connecticut, New Hampshire, New York, New Jersey, Pennsylvania, Delaware, Maryland, Virginia, North Carolina, South Carolina, Georgia.
6. France
7. All parts of Louisiana, Arkansas, Missouri, Nebraska, Iowa, South Dakota, North Dakota, Minnesota, Kansas, Oklahoma, Colorado, and Montana. Occasionally Wyoming has also been considered part of the purchase, but that claim had to be settled by separate treaty with Britain, Spain, and Russia.
8. James Knox Polk . . . before which it was an independent republic (1836-1845) and prior to that, under Mexican rule.
9. Arizona, New Mexico, California, Nevada, Utah, and Colorado west of the Rockies.
10. George Washington, admitting Vermont to the Union in 1791, Kentucky in 1792, and Tennessee in 1796.

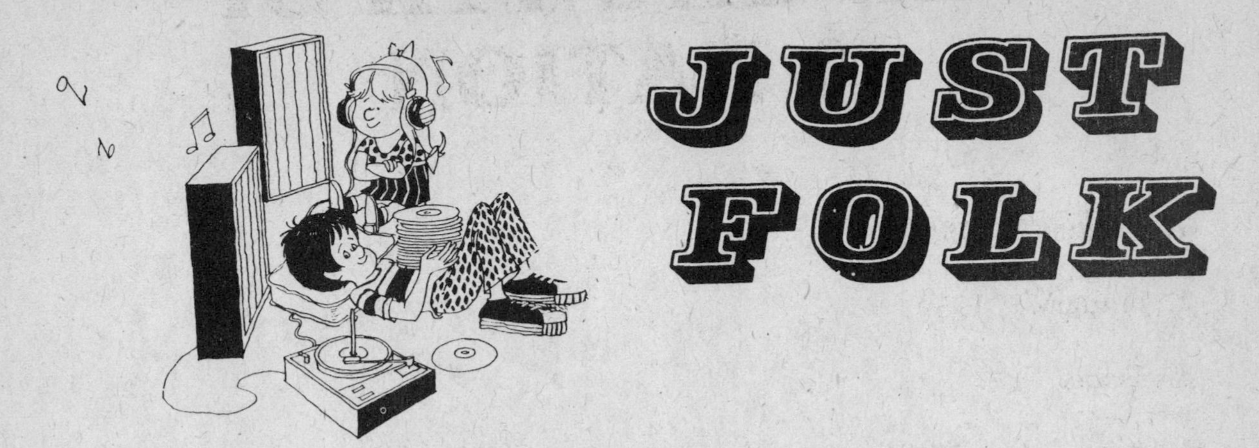

JUST FOLK

It's for sure that rock and roll had many of its roots in the folk music of the early 60s, but folk didn't exactly die as a music form when rock took over. Here are some of rock's softer-sounding cousins . . . .

1. What Minnesota-born performer started life as Robert Zimmerman?
2. Who sang protest songs with a high soprano, once dated Bob Dylan, and is too shy to eat in public?
3. For whom did Steven Stills write a song called ''Suite Judy Blue Eyes''?
4. Who wrote a song called ''Blue'' about Steven Stills?
5. Let's pursue these intertwined romances further. If ''Blue'' was for Steven Stills, for whom did Joni Mitchell write ''Willie''?
6. ''Suzanne'' and ''So Long Marianne'' are famous compositions by what tunester who also produced a novel and several books of poetry?
7. The father had a debilitating brain disease which cut off his great folk music career. The son recorded such classic tunes as ''Alice's Restaurant.'' Name both father and son.
8. What black man with a gruff voice and powerful rhythm strums is memorable for renditions of such songs as Dylan's ''Just Like A Woman'' and his own ''Freedom''?
9. What Dylan back-up band became as famous as Dylan and was the subject of the movie THE LAST WALTZ?
10. What is the name of #9's drummer, who went on to play Loretta Lynn's father in the movie COALMINER'S DAUGHTER?

JUST FOLK

(Answers)

1. Bob Dylan
2. Joan Baez
3. Judy Collins
4. Joni Mitchell
5. Graham Nash
6. Leonard Cohen
7. Woody and Arlo Guthrie
8. Richie Havens
9. The Band
10. Levon Helm

MM-MM, GOOD!

In Roman numerals, *MM* means 2000, which can be very good or very bad depending on whether you're talking about money you win as a door prize or the number of ants that raid your next picnic.

But since you never know when someone might offer you $MM if you can answer a few questions about Roman numerals, hadn't you better brush up . . . ?

1. What is signified by a dash over a Roman numeral?

2. What do we call the kind of numbers we use today instead of Roman numerals?

3. What does it mean when you put a letter after one of greater value, for instance XI?

4. What does it mean when you put a letter before one of greater value, for instance IX?

5. Write 90 in Roman numerals.

6. Write 400 in Roman numerals.

7. Write 80 in Roman numerals.

9. Write 19 in Roman numerals.

9. Write 1900 in Roman numerals.

10. Write 5000 in Roman numerals.

MM-MM, GOOD!

(Answers)

1. A dash over a numeral increases its value 1000 times, in other words, $\overline{\text{X}}$ represents 10,000.

2. Arabic numerals

3. You add the smaller number to the larger one. XI represents 11.

4. You subtract the smaller number from the larger one. IX represents 9.

5. XC

6. CD

7. LXXX

8. XIX

9. MCM

10. $\overline{\text{V}}$

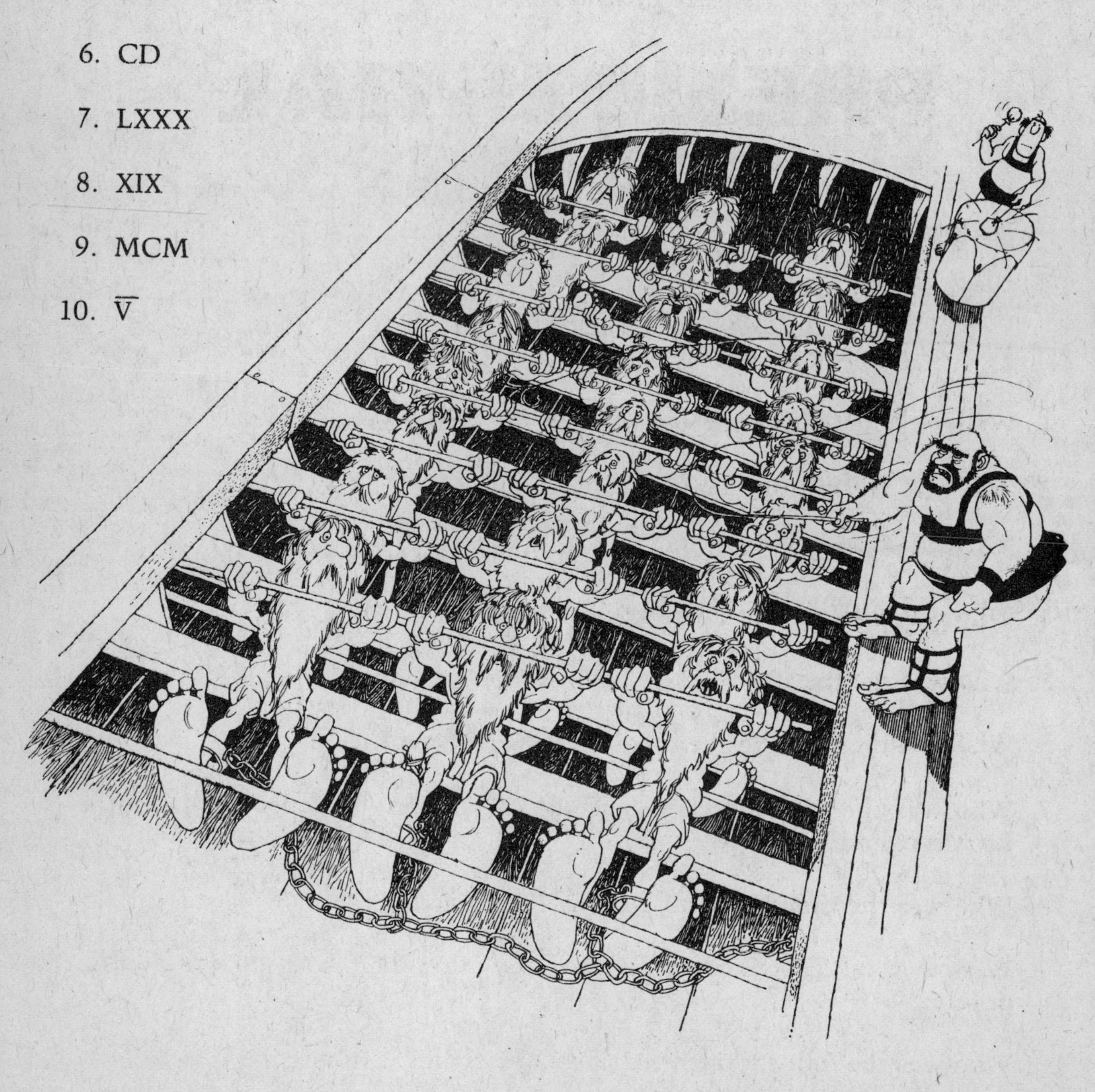

PRESIDENTIAL FIRSTS

Who was great? Who was worst? You can't always rate . . .
But you *can* know the first . . .

1. Who was the first President to live in the White House?
2. Who was the first left-handed President?
3. Who was the first President to have an original campaign song?
4. Who was the first President to use a phone?
5. Who was the first President to have a phone installed in the White House?
6. Who was the first President born in the 20th century?
7. Who was the first President born a U.S. citizen—in other words, not a British colonial subject?
8. Who was the first President born in a genuine log cabin?
9. Who was the first (and so far the only) President born on the Fourth of July?
10. Who was the first President to ride an airplane? A submarine?

PRESIDENTIAL FIRSTS

(Answers)

1. John Adams
2. James Garfield
3. Thomas Jefferson
4. James Garfield
5. Rutherford Hayes
6. John F. Kennedy
7. Martin Van Buren
8. Andrew Jackson
9. Calvin Coolidge
10. Teddy Roosevelt . . . Teddy Roosevelt

TWO PRESIDENTIAL FRIBBLES

DAVID RICE ATCHISON, born in Frogtown, Kentucky, was the unofficial President of the U.S. for one day (March 4, 1849) and the unofficial Vice-President for almost two years (April 1853-December 1854).

• He was President for a day when James K. Polk left office on a Saturday night and his successor, Zachary Taylor, delayed inaugural ceremonies until Monday for religious reasons. Atchison, president pro tempore of the Senate, unofficially held the post in the interim.

• He became Vice President under Franklin Pierce when Pierce's running mate, William King, died in office.

MIND M*A*S*H*E*R*S

If you've read the books, seen the movie, or watched the long-running series on TV, your mind is already M*A*S*H*E*D and just the right consistency to take this quiz. If not, some of these questions might be as hard to swallow as Hawkeye's hooch . . . .

1. Where does the action of M*A*S*H take place?
2. What is Hawkeye's full name and rank?
3. Why does Klinger wear a dress?
4. What's Major Margaret Houlihan's nickname?
5. In the TV series, who replaced Henry Blake as commanding officer? Who played Blake? His replacement?
6. Likewise, who replaced Trapper John as Hawkeye's best friend? Who played Trapper? His replacement?
7. What happened to Frank Burns when Margaret married a Lieutenant Colonel? What happened to the Lieutenant Colonel?
8. Who plays Hawkeye in the movie? On TV?
9. Who wrote the novel M*A*S*H?
10. Where does Major Charles Emerson Winchester come from?

MIND M*A*S*H*E*R*S

(Answers)

1. The 4077th Mobile Army Surgical Hospital in Korea
2. Captain Benjamin Franklin Pierce
3. He's trying to get a psychological discharge.
4. Hot Lips
5. Colonel Sherman Potter . . . McLean Stevenson . . . Harry Morgan
6. Captain B.J. Hunnicutt . . . Wayne Rogers . . . Mike Farrell
7. When Margaret married Lt. Col. Donald Penobscott, Frank went AWOL and was promptly transferred out of the unit . . . but it took Margaret less than a year (TV-wise) to discover that Donald was a cad, whereupon she divorced him.
8. Donald Sutherland . . . Alan Alda
9. Richard Hooker (a pseudonym)
10. Boston

WATER LOG

If you log every raft, boat, and ship that's set out to sea in the past umpteen years of movies and television, it would run longer than this whole book. So I've settled on ten of the best known, and all you have to do is match each with the show, story, or star that goes with it.

1. True Love	a. GILLIGAN'S ISLAND
2. Minnow	b. Shirley Temple
3. Cotton Blossom	c. HIGH SOCIETY
4. Pacific Princess	d. THEM
5. Good Ship Lollipop	e. SHOW BOAT
6. S.S. Viking	f. THE LOVE BOAT
7. Liberte	g. THE FRENCH LINE
8. H.M.S. Bounty	h. MR. LUCKY
9. Fortuna	i. Captain Bligh
10. Appleby	j. ENSIGN O'TOOLE

Answers:

1*c*, 2*a*, 3*e*, 4*f*, 5*b*,
6*d*, 7*g*, 8*i*, 9*h*, 10*j*

AROUND THE WORLD IN 80 FLICKS— EIGHTH LEG

Home at last! To celebrate the end of the journey, this last AROUND THE WORLD IN FLICKS matching quiz is devoted exclusively to movies set in American cities and towns. If one of them is actually where you live, go ahead and score yourself a few bonus points. If not, score yourself extra anyway—you deserve it for completing all eight parts of this cinematic excursion.

1. THE STEPFORD WIVES	a. Georgia
2. GOD'S LITTLE ACRE	b. Arizona
3. THE PETRIFIED FOREST	c. Alaska
4. STRANGE LADY IN TOWN	d. New York
5. SHAFT	e. Connecticut
6. THE SPOILERS	f. Santa Fe
7. SHANE	g. Minnesota
8. CASS TIMBERLANE	h. Florida
9. EARTHQUAKE	i. Wyoming
10. REVENGE OF THE CREATURE	j. Los Angeles

Answers: 1 *e*, 2 *a*, 3 *b*, 4 *f*, 5 *d*, 6 *c*, 7 *i*, 8 *g*, 9 *j*, 10 *h*.

BEATLEMANIA

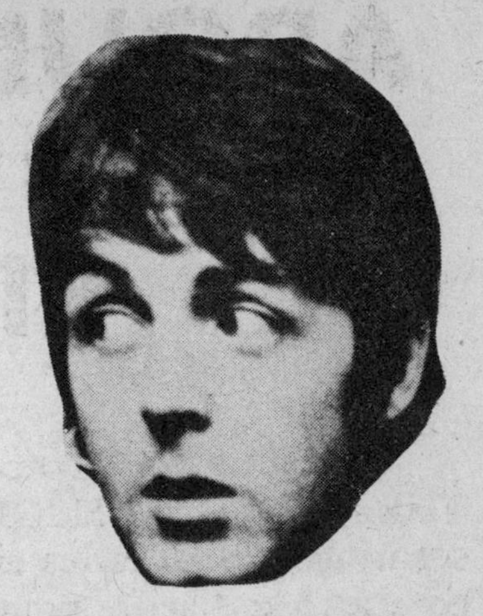

Few performers or groups have made as much of an impact on the field of pop music as four mop-headed lads from Liverpool. Their names are John, Paul, George, and Ringo. Are they the Three Stooges? The Mills Brothers? The Andrews Sisters? Heck, you know who they are—so why not, just for jollies, take this quiz about them?

1. Their first TV appearance in the U.S. almost caused a riot. Whose show were they on?
2. When George Harrison turned to Eastern mysticism, what was the name of his guru?
3. What is the name of the famous musical director who, with their manager Brian Epstein, helped to shape the Beatles' sound?
4. What is the name of the rock production company the Beatles formed in 1968, which gave rise to such stars as James Taylor, Billy Preston, and Badfinger?
5. Before the Beatles, John and Paul performed together in 1957 as ______ Twins.
6. When George joined John and Paul, the act became ______ ______ ______ ______? Then that name was changed to ______ ______ ______?
7. Which group did Ringo quit to join the Beatles? Who did he replace?
8. In which film does Paul take a bath in a coffeecup?
9. What's the name of the flashy mixed-media Broadway show featuring Beatles music and images of the 60s?
10. What was the Beatles' first film?

BEATLEMANIA

(Answers)

1. THE ED SULLIVAN SHOW (February 1964)
2. Maharishi Mahesh Yogi
3. George Martin
4. Apple
5. Nurk
6. Johnny & The Moondogs . . . The Silver Beatles
7. Rory Storme's Hurricanes . . . Pete Best
8. HELP!
9. BEATLEMANIA
10. A HARD DAY'S NIGHT

I NEVER DRINK . . . WINE!

With these well-chosen words, Count Dracula warns his victim Renfield of that fate worse than death that awaits him. Unfortunately, Mr. R. misses the point because he hasn't reviewed his vampire lore sufficiently. See that you don't make that same mistake . . . starting now!

1. Who is Bram Stoker?
2. Who was Vlad the Impaler?
3. Where is Transylvania?
4. What was the name of the first vampire film (an unauthorized version which was successfully sued by Stoker's widow for copyright infringement)?
5. In #4, what names does the central figure go by?
6. A Broadway hit became the 1979 movie DRACULA. Who played Dracula in both play and film?
7. In Bela Lugosi's classic version of the film DRACULA, who plays the female lead?
8. In HOUSE OF FRANKENSTEIN, what other screen monsters share the bill with the Count?
9. Who plays Dracula in #8?
10. Bela Lugosi is certainly the most famous screen Dracula. After him, the name most frequently associated with the role—star of DRACULA AD and THE SATANIC RITES OF DRACULA, etc. is _________ _________ ?

I NEVER DRINK . . . WINE!

(Answers)

1. The author of DRACULA
2. A 15th-century Romanian prince said to be the inspiration for the Dracula legend
3. In Romania
4. NOSFERATU
5. Orlok
6. Frank Langella
7. Helen Chandler
8. The Wolfman and the Frankenstein Monster
9. John Carradine
10. Christopher Lee

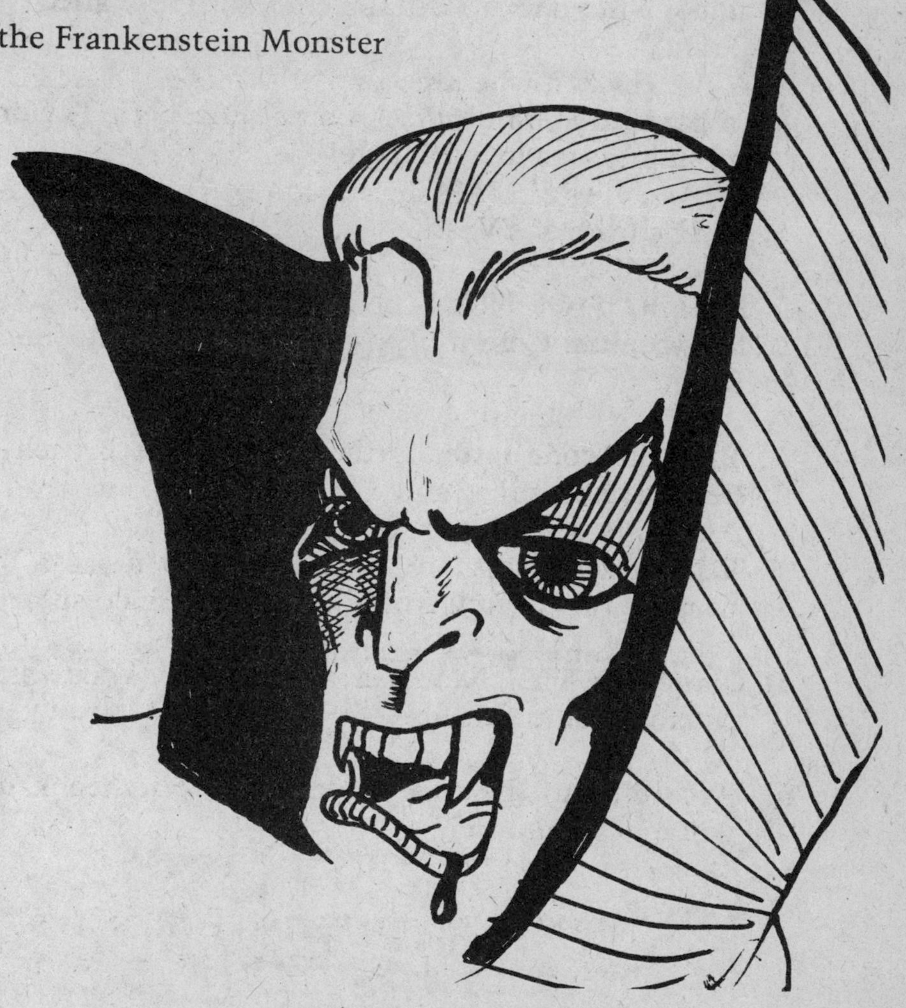

Each of these answers involves a letter of the alphabet, or a few, but nothing you'd go so far as to call a whole word. Now are you convinced we've covered *Trivia A-Z*?

1. What's Peter Lorre's classic flick about a homocidal madman brought to justice by the Berlin underworld?

2. Name the Yves Montand movie about the assassination of a Greek pacifist.

3. Duke Ellington's swing theme song is called "Take the __________ Train."

4. What film stars Michael Caine, Elizabeth Taylor and Susannah York in an unpleasant love triangle?

5. A short-lived TV show of the late 70s was called MR. __________ AND TINA.

6. The popular military slang term for German submarines is __________-boats.

7. By what code letter is the head of the British SIS (Secret Intelligence Service) known?

8. What two letters are considered the newest in the English language because they weren't used until after Shakespeare?

9. Name the Paul Newman and Joanne Woodward movie about a super-patriotic radio station.

10. According to the title of an Alfred Hitchcock movie, what number do you dial for murder?

Answers: 1. M, 2. Z, 3. A, 4. XY & Zee, 5. T, 6. U, 7. C, 8. J & V, 9. WUSA, 10. M

DON ELMO HAS WRITTEN OTHER TRIVIA BOOKS UNDER ANOTHER NAME! JOHN FEELEY, THE FEATURED ILLUSTRATOR, IS THIS GUY I'M DRAWING!

THE WORLD'S FIRST OFFICIAL FRIBBLE QUIZ

That's right. This is the first one. So far, there isn't a second one. That makes this the only one. Score two or better on it and you're entitled to fill in *your own name* on the MASTER OF FRIBBLOLOGY DEGREE which appears on the other side of this page. Then you will never again get into trouble for practicing fribblology without a license.

1. Who is older, Peter Fonda or Jane Fonda?
2. What is the first name of the actress who plays Mary Richards' "Aunt Flo" on the MARY TYLER MOORE SHOW?
3. Which of the Cooper girls does Valerie Bertinelli play on TV's ONE DAY AT A TIME?
4. What is the name of the inflatable rubber Automatic Pilot in the movie AIRPLANE?
5. Did you like this book?

Answers:

1. Jane
2. Eileen
3. Barbara
4. Otto
5. Yes